100 Challenging Go Problems

for

100 Days of Study

The Best of *Kido's* Dan/Kyu Ranking Tests

Edited by the Nihon Ki-in

Published by
Yutopian Enterprises
2255 29th Street
Santa Monica, CA 90405
1-800-YUTOGO-3
yutopian@netcom.com

Originally published in Japanese by the Nihon Ki-in under the title of **Hyaku-nichi Tanoshimeru Hyaku-dai**. Translated by R.J. Terry.

Words in brackets [ ] indicate translation notes.

...Be strong and of good courage;
be not frightened, neither be dismayed;
for the Lord your God is with you wherever you go.
Josh. 1:9 RSV

First printing September 1995

Foreword

The Dan/Kyu Test in *Kido* magazine made its first appearance in the April 1950 issue. Although today the title has been changed to "The Challenge Corner," for roughly thirty years the tests have garnered popularity with one and all as a challenge of go strength.

Contained within it are knotty problems that even professionals would tend to answer incorrectly. Offbeat problems are also here, and cases where those with the actual playing strength of an amateur 5 dan would find it quite difficult to pass muster as shodan are frequent. To that extent, if one passes the test, then there can be no quibbling about one's ranking. By the same token, it is a fact that one can proudly announce that ranking wherever one goes.

Incorporated in this book are a special selection of 100 problems that have been culled from those presented over the past ten years. Speaking of the characteristics of the problems, they have been divided into eight sections: The Opening, The Middlegame, Perception, Sabaki [Fancy Footwork], Reading, Race to Capture [Semeai], Life and Death, and The Endgame. But there is absolutely no reason to feel compelled to begin with Problem Number 1 and work out each of them in order. It is fine to turn to whichever section one wishes to work on as the spirit moves one. The idea is that if each day one works on a different problem, in the end one will have spent 100 days in satisfying study.

The success rate of those respondents who mailed in answers to the magazine at the time for each of the problems has been appended here, but please bear in mind that the great majority of the original problems were offered without the broad hints regarding the focal points that have been given in this book. Ultra-difficult problems that amassed a respondent success rate of less than 1% have been omitted.

In this book one can grasp trends in previous problems as well as a number of points useful in solving them, and if that aids the reader in solving future problems in the magazine, we will be gratified. Keep your fighting spirit up.

The Nihon Ki-in, Editorial Department

KIDO magazine: Special Edition

**Kido Dan/Kyu Ranking Test
Special Problem Selection**

100 Challenging Problems
for
100 Days of Study

Table of Contents

Supervision: Haruyama Isamu 9 dan

Editor: Satatsu Yasuhiro

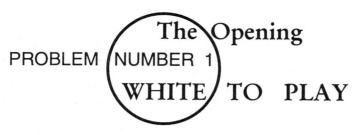

The Opening
PROBLEM NUMBER 1
WHITE TO PLAY

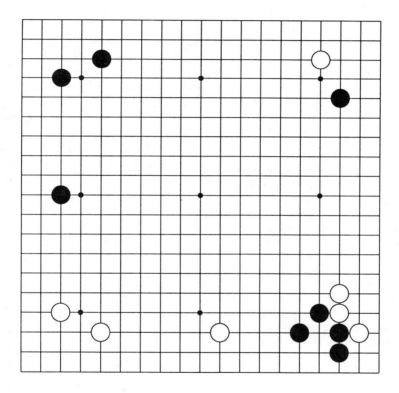

The game has just barely begun. In the lower right corner, a joseki is in progress.

One ponders what the best move to play here for white is. Please reflect well on the placement of stones in the upper right, as well as on the lower side.

(12% respondent success rate)

Solution

A Golden-plated Turning Move

Solution Diagram One can sometimes take an unfocused view of the opening, reasoning to oneself that joseki moves are the correct ones to adopt, *just because* they are joseki. But that can be wrong. One must regularly vary one's approach according to the surrounding positions.

Here white must pay attention to black's attacking marked stone in the upper right, and see that turning at 1 is the best thing to do. When black hanes at 2, white presses with 3 & 5, and using this thickness as a backdrop, plays white 7 as both a pincer and an extension: an ideal point.

Diagram 1 (Black incurs a disadvantage) Black may perhaps be dissatisfied with the course of events that would follow the white turning move at 1, but playing first on the right side at black 2 invokes a severe response from white in the form of the fencing-in move of 3. Black cannot fail to respond with 4 & 6, which means that black has sealed white in and kept sente as well. Letting white's lower side become this thick and powerful is unacceptable.

Diagram 2 (Too easygoing) White 1 is joseki, but it is played haphazardly here. Black occupies the key point on the right side with 2, and now there is no clear attack to direct at black. A white move at **a** is hardly better: black will attack the corner again at **b**.

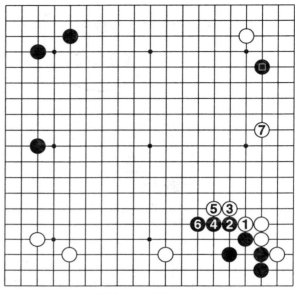

Solution Diagram

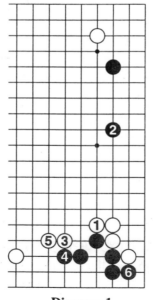

Diagram 1

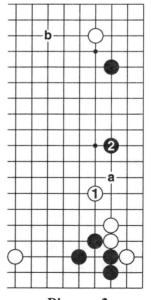

Diagram 2

8

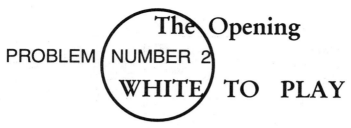

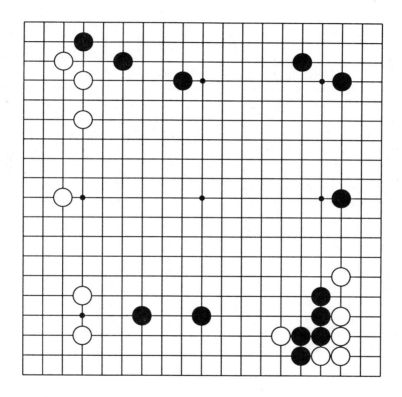

The Opening

PROBLEM NUMBER 2

WHITE TO PLAY

A quite ordinary opening is under way, but for white's next move, what is the best thing to do?

Sometimes, the strongest action that one can take is to choose a defensive play, which, nevertheless, contains a hidden aim.

(14% respondent success rate)

Solution

A Calm and Collected Extending Move

Solution Diagram The extending move of white 1 in the lower right is correct. Solidly stabilizing the shape in this way is the vital point in this board position.

In response, defending at black 2 is par for the course. Neglecting to play this move would allow white to attack with the jump at **a**, which is white's aim in playing at 1. After this, it may be imagined that white will look for new fields to plow, and take the first shot at playing on the upper side at 3. If white had first played at 3 instead of 1, black would press white down vigorously with **b**, white 1, black **c**, white **d**, and black **e**, creating magnificent thickness on the lower side which would then be practically inviolable.

Diagram 1 (Too hasty) Rushing to attack with the jump of white 1 may be acceptable in special circumstances. In this position, black will push at 2 and finish up with 6. Following this, white will have to manage the safety of the three stones somehow [sabaki], a burden which will restrain white from operating on the upper side.

Diagram 2 (Black is doing well) Pushing at white 1 is insufficient. When black plays 2, white can hane at 3, but then 5 can not be omitted, and white is saddled with gote. After this, black can gain further advantage by playing **a**, white **b**, black **c**, and the only thing that white has accomplished is to help black build a large territory on the lower side.

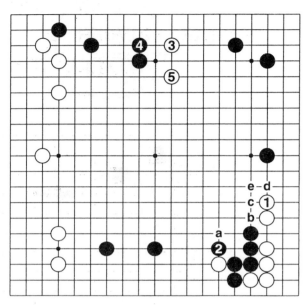

Solution Diagram

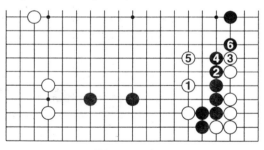

Diagram 1

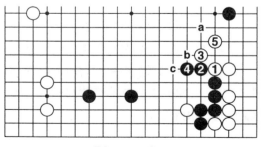

Diagram 2

10

The Opening
PROBLEM NUMBER 3
BLACK TO PLAY

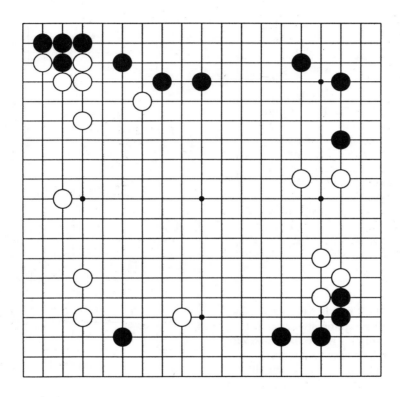

In this board position, white's growing territorial framework (moyo) on the left is the cause of much concern.

What kind of plan must black adopt to reduce this territory? In addition to this mandate, one must be sensitive to the nuances of the position.

(6% respondent success rate)

Solution

Rip Right Through

Solution Diagram If white's marked stone on the lower side connects with the corner, Then white's large territorial framework [moyo] on the left side becomes deep. Here one must first intuitively grasp that cutting the connection is the primary concern, since mediocre technique has minimal effect on white.

Black presses white with the fencing in move of 1. The loose nature of the diagonal jump may seem all too dangerous, but if white obligingly strikes at the gap, black pushes through at 3 & 5 and black's aim in the present board position has been accomplished. Through black 11, white's corner has been solidified, but black's territory on the lower side is also large, and what is more, black has a head up and pointed at white's large territorial framework [moyo], which has great significance.

Diagram 1 (White is well off) If black plays the mediocre jump at 1, after playing white 2, the knight's move of 4 is severe. The pincer of the marked white stone works effectively, and it is inevitable that black's stones will face an excruciatingly difficult battle.

Diagram 2 (White's large territorial framework [moyo] is superior) Entering the 3-3 point with black 1 is an idea with a great deal of common sense behind it. The profit that black makes with the moves through 7 is by no means small, but white's large territorial framework [moyo] is far and away superior to it.

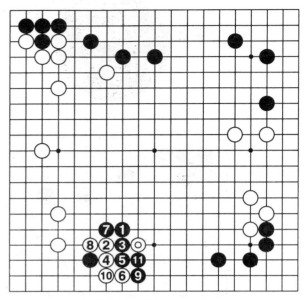

Solution Diagram

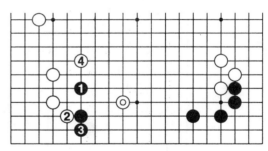

Diagram 1

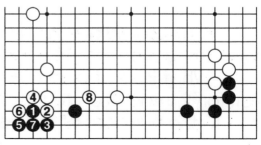

Diagram 2

12

PROBLEM NUMBER 4 — The Opening — WHITE TO PLAY

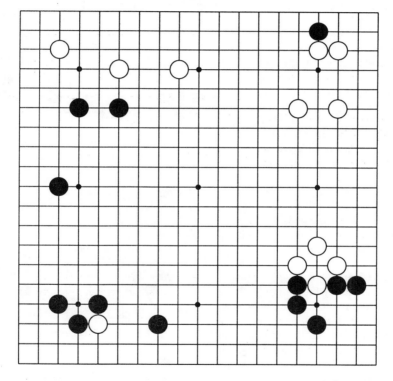

In this game, both sides are in competition to develop their respective large territorial frameworks (moyo).

At this stage in the struggle, where is the absolutely ideal point that may be considered the pivotal spot to occupy?

(22% respondent success rate)

Solution

A Jump with a Commanding View

Solution Diagram In games where large territorial frameworks [moyo] contend with each other, moves that expand one's own framework while at the same time reducing the opponent's become most important.

In this board position, the jump at white 1 is correct. In short, this is a vital point that is related to the fortunes of both frameworks, and one might say that with it white has the commanding view. If black defends the side with 2, white makes a further jump to 3, and white's framework becomes all the more grand and imposing.

When playing with the same intention, white **a** is heavy, while the hane at **b** is questionable, since black will cut at **a**. The jump to white 1 is best.

Diagram 1 (Black is badly off) If black plays elsewhere when white jumps with the marked stone, then settling the shape with white 1 through 5 is satisfying. After this, if black plays **a**, white has the technique of **b**, black **c**, and white **d** available, and regardless of anything else, black's position has been flattened here.

Diagram 2 (A big difference) Let's see what happens when the reverse happens, and black gets to play here first. The two-step hane of 1 & 3 is severe, and the sequence through 9 can be predicted. The difference between this variation and the **Solution Diagram** is quite evident.

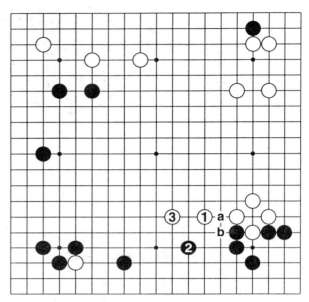

Solution Diagram

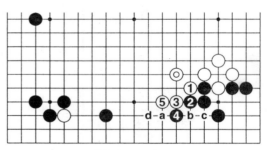

Diagram 1

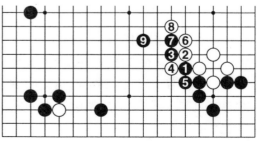

Diagram 2

14

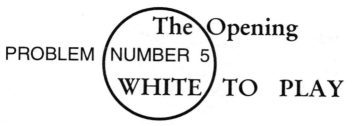

The Opening

PROBLEM NUMBER 5

WHITE TO PLAY

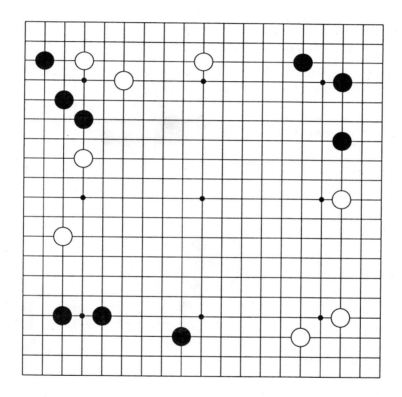

There are good points on the upper side, the left side and on the lower side that meet the eye, but among those points there is one that must be seen as being particularly urgent.

(48% respondent success rate)

Solution

An Essential Point for Attack and Defense

Solution Diagram In the opening one must pay special attention to the base and stability of stones. That is because being saddled with unstable stones means that a disadvantage incurred continues to plague one unabated into the middlegame.

In this board position, white is thin on the left side. Consequently, the diagonal move of white 1 is an essential play that takes precedence over other big points. Furthermore, the move of white 1 does not only defend the left side, but it is also important in that it threatens black's base in the corner. If black defends the corner with 2, white can be satisfied at that, and turn to play at 3 on the lower side, getting to the big point there first.

Diagram 1 (White is doing well) If black plays elsewhere in answer to the marked white diagonal move, the attack with the extending move of white 1 is severe. When black plays 2, white torments the group with 3 and the moves that follow, and the black stones are still not completely secure. Instead of white 3, an attachment at 6 is also possible.

Diagram 2 (Scooping out the side in sente) If, in reverse, black plays first here and gets to invade the left side at 1, it is a one-sided defensive game for white. Scooping out the left side in sente through white 8 makes this a big difference for both sides.

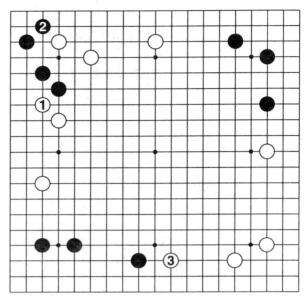

Solution Diagram

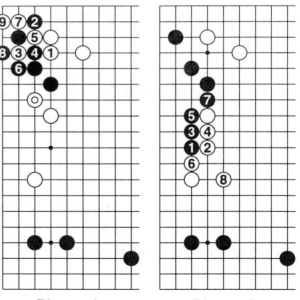

Diagram 1   **Diagram 2**

16

The Opening
PROBLEM NUMBER 6
BLACK TO PLAY

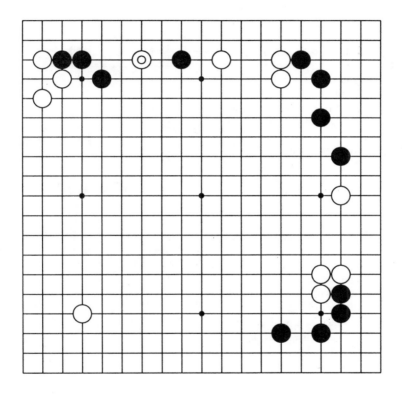

At this point, white has just invaded with the marked stone on the upper side. What is the best way for black to respond?

This is not a question that concerns capturing white's marked stone.

(14% respondent success rate)

Solution

Seek a Way to Take the Initiative

Solution Diagram If one seeks to capture white's invading marked stone directly, it will not go well. At times like this, using a two-pronged attack is a better strategy.

The fencing in move of black 1, which probes white's response, is correct here. If white replies with the diagonal move at 2 in order to push outward, black gets the initiative to attack at 3. Then if white moves out with 4, black forces [kikashi] by pushing at 5, and then blocking at 7 hits the right spot precisely. If events proceed in this way, white's two stones have had all the life in them snuffed out.

Diagram 1 (White cannot be captured) If black immediately tries to capture white by playing the diagonal move of 1, white will not docilely abandon the stone. Instead, white will kick up a ruckus within the black position with 2 & 4, and then later the moves at 10 & 12 comprise a wonderfully adroit finesse [tesuji]. In the end, an exchange [furi-kawari] results with the sequence through 17, but though black makes thickness on the outside, the dissatisfaction that black must feel over failing to capture the white stones after all can be imagined.

Diagram 2 (Sufficient for white) If black plays the attachment of 1, white simply connects underneath with the move at 2 and the following. After this, if black plays at **a**, white answers at **b**. The original invasion of the marked white stone in the **Solution Diagram** has been a success.

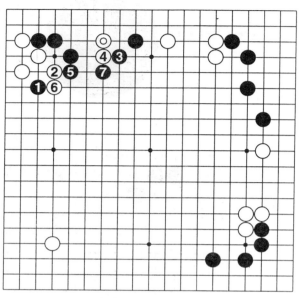

Solution Diagram

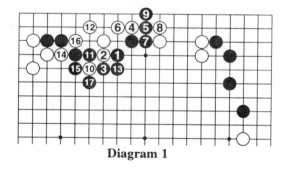

Diagram 1

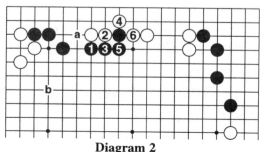

Diagram 2

18

The Opening
PROBLEM NUMBER 7
BLACK TO PLAY

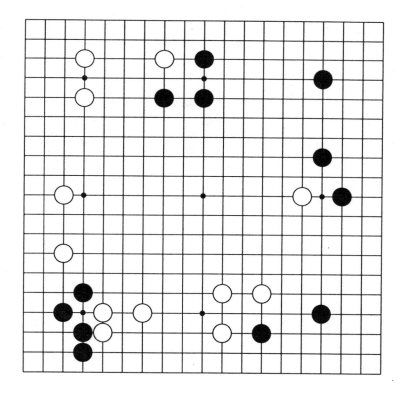

In this position, one must decide which is more important: attack or defense?

Black's large territorial framework (moyo) in the upper right may not yet be said to be real territory. And in so saying...

(13% respondent success rate)

Solution

A Move that Makes Great Profit

Solution Diagram White's large territorial framework [moyo] on the left is also big, but if the upper right framework can be converted into definite territory, black can expect to realize profit equal to that area and then some.

In this board position, the reinforcement of black 1 in the upper right is the largest move. With this one move, black can look forward to accruing a considerable amount of territory in the upper right quadrant. Playing at black **a** or **b** instead of 1 would leave white with a move at the 3-3 point, and thus be lax. Furthermore, the fencing in move of black **d** is an energetic move, but white's marked stone is light and easily expendable. In that case too, white would invade the 3-3 point at **c**.

Diagram 1 (Problems [aji] remain) The diagonal move of black 1 is also a good point, but to the extent that it spreads out one space wider on the upper side, it leaves scope for action in the corner. For instance, after invading at 2, white enters the corner at 4, and after 8, if black next plays at **a**, it is a simple matter for white to start ko with the reply at **b**.

Diagram 2 (Too big) If black does not make a move to defend this area, the white invasion of the 3-3 point with 1 is big. When black blocks at 2, white runs rampant in the corner with the moves following 3, and the territory white gains there cannot be sneezed at either.

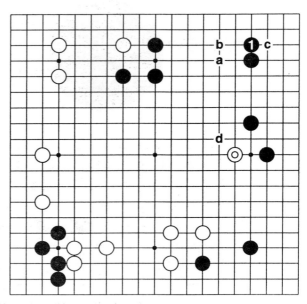

Solution Diagram

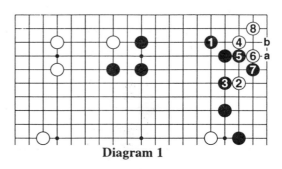

Diagram 1

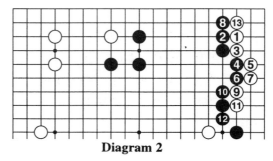

Diagram 2

20

The Opening

PROBLEM NUMBER 8

BLACK TO PLAY

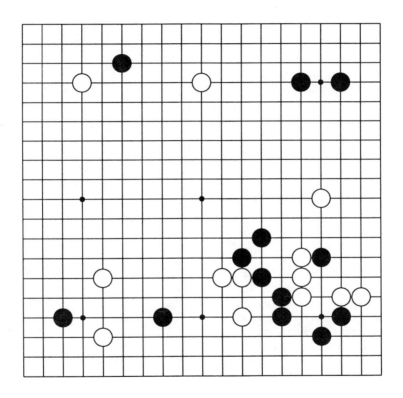

There are various points on the board that strike the eye as being big, but here the operative words may come from the go proverb that states: "Take the critical point rather than the big point."

(24% respondent success rate)

Solution

A Preemptive Attack

Solution Diagram It does not matter whether one is analyzing the opening or the middlegame, a vital area that is directly related to an attack on either side's stones must regularly take precedence over a simple big point.

In this board position, the vital place to play is on the lower side. The correct thing to do is to play the fencing in move of black 1, a preemptive strike against white's three stones, before the marked black stone comes under attack. If white moves out at 2, it will be possible to run away. However, with the moves from black 3 through 7, white's shape is not only crippled, but after black turns to play at 9, the thickness that black has created will now be useful in attacking white's position to the left.

Diagram 1 (Dissatisfaction) Anything besides the fencing in move would fail to attack accurately. The commonplace jump to black 1 would conversely incur the fencing in move of white 2, letting white take a good initiative and an easy position to play. Instead of black 1 here, black **a**, white **b**, black **c**, white 2, and black **d**, invites white **e**, and no matter what happens, this cannot be considered a suitable attack.

Diagram 2 (Very bad) If black languidly plays the ordinary jump to 1 on the left, capping at white 2 is the vital point. To have the tables turned and go from the offense to the defense by allowing this ideal move, means that however favorable a game black had before, the game cannot be won now.

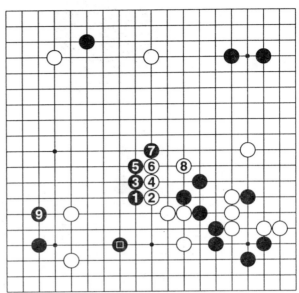

Solution Diagram

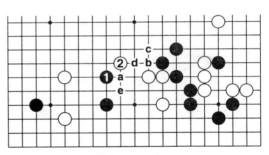

Diagram 1

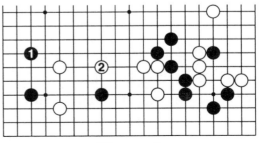

Diagram 2

PROBLEM **The** O**pening**

NUMBER 9

WHITE TO PLAY

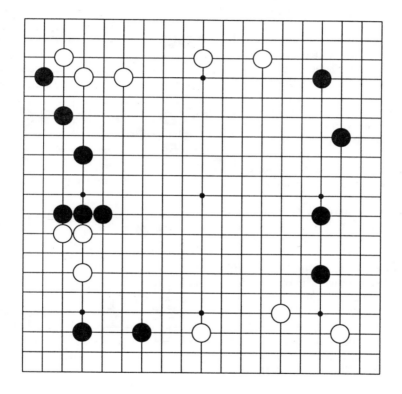

The three white stones in the lower left are a quintessential model of thin shape. The way to defend this white group is the theme.

(30% respondent success rate)

Solution

Settle the Group with an Attachment

Solution Diagram Since white cannot look forward to profitably running out into the center with the three stones in the lower left, the best thing to do is to settle the group here.

It is most appropriate to go all the way in to make the attachment at white 1. If black hanes outward at 2, white plays the cross-cut of 3. Black's position on the lower side is not strong enough to allow strenuous resistance, so the variation following 4 is inevitable. Up to 11, white achieves success in encroaching upon black's corner, while settling the left side group. If, at some point during this sequence, such as at 4 or 6, black plays the atari at 7 to start a fight, white extends to 6, and it cannot be imagined that white will be at a disadvantage.

Diagram 1 (White is thin) It is insufficiently aggressive for white to play the more restrained knight's move at 1. When black answers at 2, white makes a settled shape for the group, more or less, with 3 & 5, but black is left with such unpleasant measures as the placement at **a** and the hane and connection starting with **b**. In addition, when black's group on the lower side becomes strengthened to this extent, the possibility [aji] of an invasion to the right at **c** is produced.

Diagram 2 (An ideal attack) If white plays elsewhere in this position, the attack of black 1 & 3 is ideal. When this happens, white has no choice but to run out into the center.

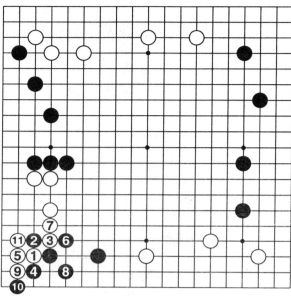

Solution Diagram

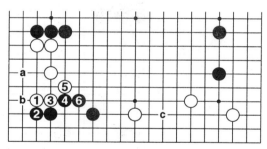

Diagram 1

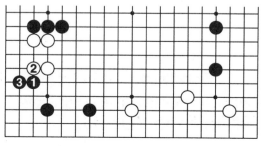

Diagram 2

24

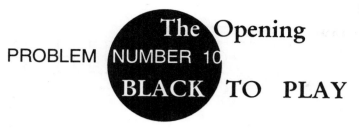

The Opening

PROBLEM NUMBER 10

BLACK TO PLAY

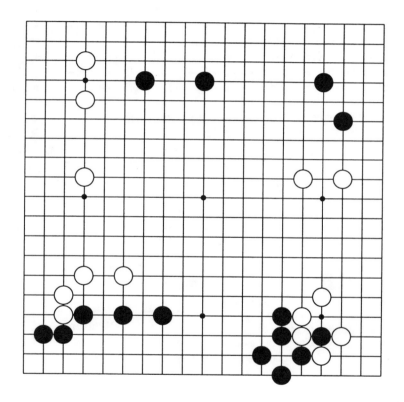

One must focus in on the critical sector or one will fail.

There is an ideal point here that may be truly called the crucial one in this opening.

(39% respondent success rate)

Solution

An Ideal Fencing in Move

Solution Diagram The fencing in knight's move of black 1 in the lower right is, without question, an ideal point. With this single move, white's territory on the right side suddenly becomes flattened, while on the contrary, black's large territorial framework [moyo] on the lower side swells larger. Two, or even three birds are killed with this one stone. It is galling to white to have to defend at 2, but there is little choice about it, and black gets to jump to 3, controlling the initiative more and more firmly.

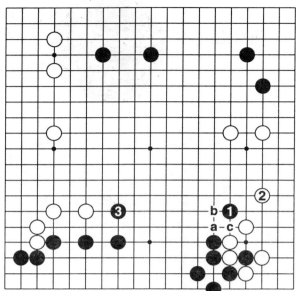

Solution Diagram

Instead of black 1, extending to **a** or jumping to **b** do not put enough pressure on white, while an atari at black **c** eliminates possibilities [aji keshi] that black has in this area. Fencing white in with black 1 is the only move here.

Diagram 1 (A loose ladder) White cannot counterattack against black's fencing in move of 1 with the technique of playing the hane outward with 2. Black cuts at 3 and then fences white's stone in with 5, capturing it. Now, if white tries to move out at **a**, black captures white in a loose ladder with **b**, white **c**, and black **d**.

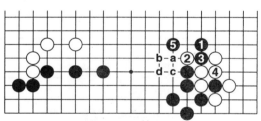

Diagram 1

Diagram 2 (A commanding view) If black overlooks that vital point here, it is natural that white would play the hane of 1 against black's position. In reply to black 2, white plays 3 through 9. It is clear, in comparison with the variation shown in the **Solution Diagram**, that either side would take a commanding view of the situation by playing in this area first.

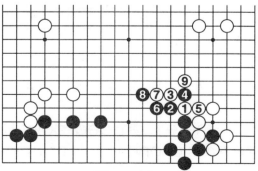

Diagram 2

26

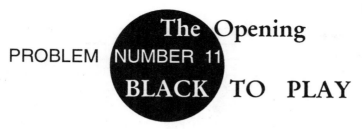

The Opening

PROBLEM NUMBER 11

BLACK TO PLAY

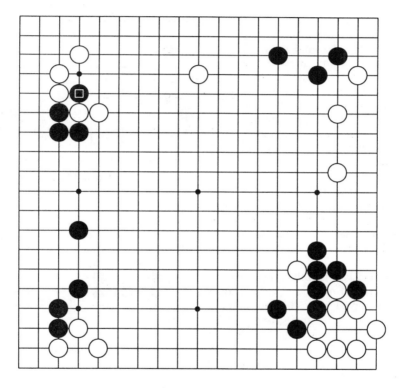

In this position, one's attention is directed to black's large territorial framework (moyo) on the left side. How to enhance this position is the subject, as well as the role that black's marked stone, which is not yet completely devoid of life, can play.

(19% respondent success rate)

Solution

Fencing White in is the Vital Point

Solution Diagram The marked black stone is not completely dead, but trying to drag it out directly would only give white a target to attack.

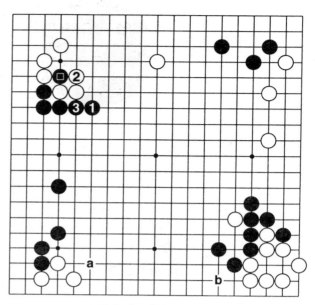

Solution Diagram

The fencing in move of black 1 is without question the vital point. If white eliminates any question of moving out with this stone by playing at 2, black connects solidly with 3, making thickness that works ideally on the left side, and any number of weak points remain to be exploited [aji] to limit white's territory on the upper side.

The pincer attack of black **a** on the lower side also seems to have merit as the basis of a powerful plan, but one must feel dissatisfaction since the lower side is open at the point of **b**.

Diagram 1 (Black is well off) When playing the fencing in move at 1, black hopes that white will push at 2. The hane at 3 lets black build a stronger and stronger initiative. The moves through white 8 solidify the upper side, but at the same time black's left side is becoming that much more thick, and black ends up with sente.

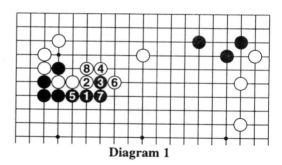

Diagram 1

Diagram 2 (A good fight) Shifting black 1 a single space deeper produces a play that is a kind of a finesse [tesuji], but the counterattack of white 2 & 4 is unavoidable. After white defends at 6 & 8, handling the two black stones becomes a problem, and this variation lacks the clarity of the **Solution Diagram**.

Diagram 2

28

The Opening

PROBLEM NUMBER 12

BLACK TO PLAY

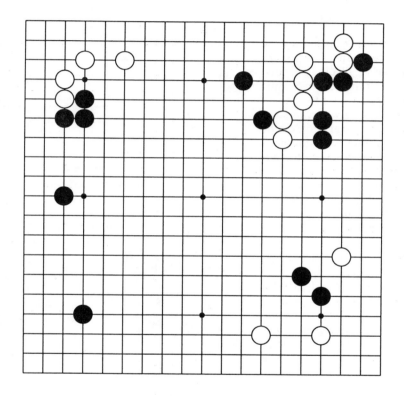

The shape in the upper right and the lower right is a cause for concern. Where might the essential point for attack and defense be?

One must not blunder and play a point just adjacent to the correct one.

(31% respondent success rate)

Solution

The Large Knight's Move Works Perfectly

Solution Diagram The problem here is to determine how white will move out with the marked stone on the right side. It would not be good to make things too easy for white.

The correct answer is to play the checking extension of the large knight's move of black 1, a good move that protects black above, while giving support to black's two stones below, and attacking white. In addition, the black diagonal move on the upper side at **a** will be a severe attack on the white group on the upper side. But if white avoids that by playing at **b**, black can start to swallow white's marked stone by playing at **c**. If white then attaches at **d**, black plays at **e**, and black 1 is effective.

Diagram 1 (A one space difference) Black 1 placed a space from the correct point makes it easy for white to handle [sabaki] the marked stone. Approaching closely might seem to be more severe, but after white 2 & 4, black 5 cannot be omitted. Also, the tight move of black **a** would give white's marked stone more room to maneuver.

Diagram 2 (Mistaken direction) Attaching in the lower right corner with black 1 shows a mistake in direction. Through 8, white secures the right side, then attacks at the vital point of 10. Black **a**, white **b**, black **c**, and white **d** next results in a difficult position for black.

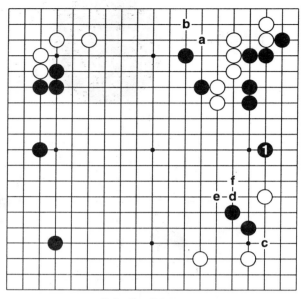

Solution Diagram

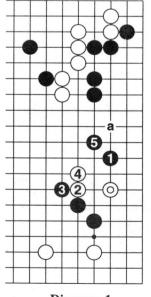

Diagram 1

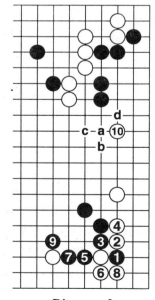

Diagram 2

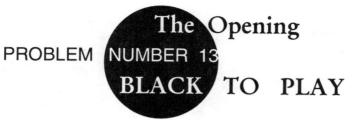

The Opening

PROBLEM NUMBER 13

BLACK TO PLAY

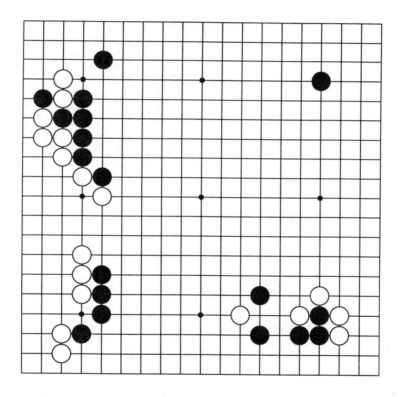

The whole lower side, and into the center, looks somehow or other like it is black's. What is the best plan for black to adopt here.

It is not necessary to think too deeply about complexities in this situation.

(33% respondent success rate)

31

Solution

A Simple Atari

Solution Diagram Black is pushing white on the third and fourth lines above and below in the process of making walls on the left side. If black can manage to effectively connect the two walls in the center, the thickness thereby gained would triple or quadruple in value at a single stroke.

The correct move to play here is the atari of black 1, forcing white to connect at 2, and then after the atari of black 3, crude though it is, black can finish off by pushing at 5 & 7, and this is altogether a simple and clear sequence. White has no scope for divergence in this variation and there is no question that black perfects a large territorial framework [moyo] which is impressive in size.

Diagram 1 (Insufficient) If black insists on playing the "proper" move, the hane of 1, things will not be simple. After white 2 & 4, black might extend at 5 aiming to seal white in, but the attachment of white 6 drives a wedge in black's wall, leading to the variation through 18. Although thick, black's freedom of movement on the lower side is restricted. Black has no way at all to attack the three white stones in the center.

Diagram 2 (Small) Considering half-measures like black 1 is not good. White plays 2 & 4 in the center, and if now black captures with **a**, white **b** is a good point.

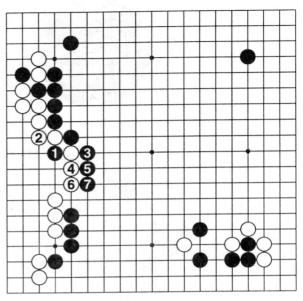

Solution Diagram

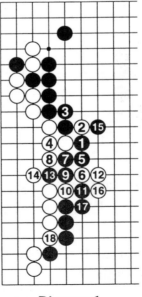

Diagram 1

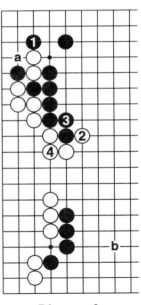

Diagram 2

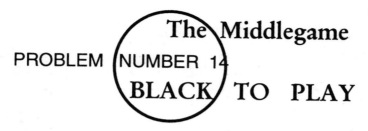

The Middlegame
PROBLEM NUMBER 14
BLACK TO PLAY

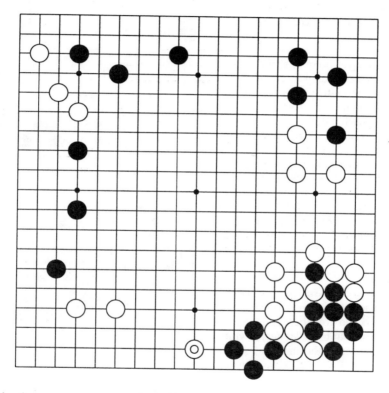

We have come, by the by, to plunge into the position here which is one in the middlegame. At this juncture, white has pressed in with the marked stone. How would one suppose black best answer? There is no skill involved in merely running out to the center.

(18% respondent success rate)

Solution

Sacrifice Four Stones

Solution Diagram If one constantly responds according to the opponent's whims, there will be no way to grasp the winning chance. In this board position it is necessary to intuitively view the four black stones on the lower side as light and easily discarded.

The correct thing to do in this situation is to play the fencing in move of black 1. Even though black is prepared to sacrifice the four stones on the lower side, such a course of action would not be cause for regret. If white pushes up with 2, black 3 holds the two stones in check, and after white 4, black plays 5. At this point, the moves following white 6, whereby black discards the four stones, are inevitable, and an exchange [furi-kawari] results where black takes full compensation by capturing white's stone in a ladder with 11.

Diagram 1 (No cause for dissatisfaction) If white hanes at 4 in response to black 1 & 3, black cuts at 5 and now there is no necessity to discard the four black stones. If white continues with 6 & 8, the move at 9 finishes up an ideal dodging maneuver [sabaki].

Diagram 2 (Too easygoing) The capping move of black 1 is, understandably, lacking in forcefulness. When white counterattacks with 2 and the following, black is able to escape with the moves up to 19, but managing to do anything [sabaki] with black's three stones that have been cut off will be a problem.

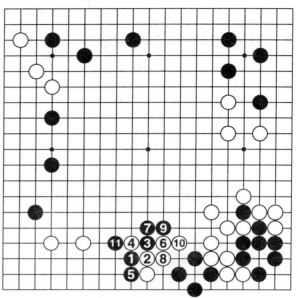

Solution Diagram

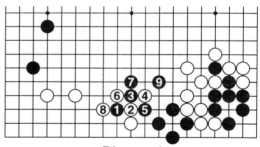

Diagram 1

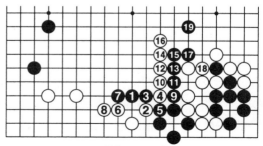

Diagram 2

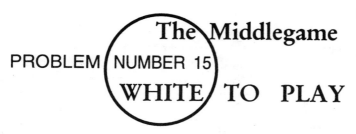

The Middlegame

PROBLEM NUMBER 15

WHITE TO PLAY

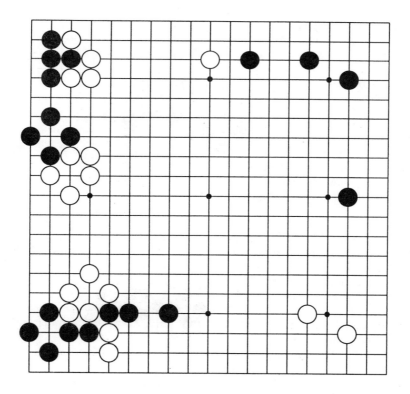

If the area that one's eye comes to rest upon is the incorrect one, the solution will prove elusive.

Should one aim at playing the most common sense type of big point, or is there perhaps a more severe move that can be adopted?

(15% respondent success rate)

Solution

Wedge into the Position on the Lower Side

Solution Diagram In middle-game problems there are few cases where the solution is directly concerned with simple extensions or checking moves that stabilize groups of stones. In the problem here, playing the checking extension of **a** or the jump to **b** is insufficient.

The correct move is white 1, wedging into the black position on the lower side. If black plays atari from above with 2, white 3 through 7 save white's two stones and makes a big profit. Furthermore, according to the circumstances in the game, white may even look forward to attacking the black stones in the center of the board.

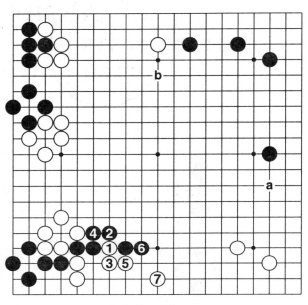

Solution Diagram

Diagram 1 (White's dream) In response to white's wedge at 1, playing 2 from below leaves black badly off. White is delighted to extend to 3, and after black 4, cut at 5. After this, pushing through with black **a** is impossible, and the low position of black's stones after **b**, white **c**, black **d**, white **e** would be unbearable. White can only dream of getting the chance to play the variation in this diagram.

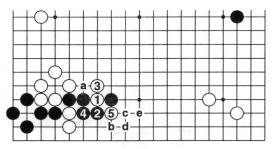

Diagram 1

Diagram 2 (Second best) The checking extension of white 1 is also a strong move. Black will probably defend at 2, in which case white carries on with a strategy of sacrificing two stones to give preference to developing the center with 3 & 5.

In any event, allowing black to play on the lower side first would be bad.

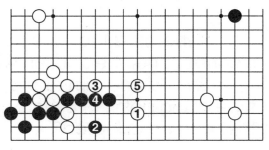

Diagram 2

36

The Middlegame

PROBLEM NUMBER 16

WHITE TO PLAY

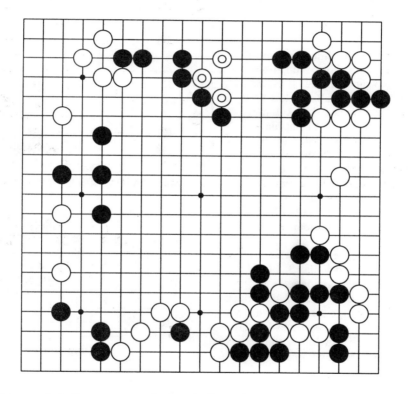

The middlegame is in full swing, and the question is how white is to manage to get the marked stones on the upper side out of difficulty (sabaki).

It is also necessary to read with a vision of the whole board.

(58% respondent success rate)

Solution

The Simple Hane is the Correct Form

Solution Diagram The theme here is the adroit management [sabaki] of white's three stones on the upper side. As may be expected, allowing black to take all of the territory here would be bad.

Considering that white has effective ko threats available, the simple hane at 1 is a good move. If black cuts at 2, white naturally makes ko with 3, and in answer to black 4, the ko threats at white 5 & 11 put black in a tight spot. In the middle of this sequence, if black ends the ko with 6, white captures the lower side with the connection at 6 and can feel satisfied. After white takes the ko at 13, black can cut to the right of white's marked stone, but that is insufficient as a ko threat.

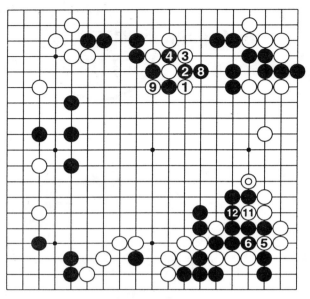

Solution Diagram   7, 10, 13: take ko

Diagram 1 (Squeezed) If white jumps to 1, after black 2 and white 3, black shuns playing ko and instead connects at 4, planning to tough it out. White 5 and black 6 are both the strongest moves, and when white cuts at 7, black sacrifices five stones to put the squeeze on white with the moves following black 8. Compared to the **Solution Diagram**, white is worse off.

Diagram 1

Diagram 2 (Crude play) Cutting with white 1 and then playing atari with 3 is bad form. In reply to black 4, the hanging connection of white 5 is perhaps the standard play here, but the poke of black 6 leaves white in a quandary. Please confirm for yourself that a black move at **a**, which limits what white can do on the outside, is also sente against the white corner.

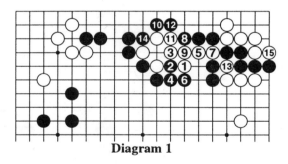

Diagram 2

38

The Middlegame

PROBLEM NUMBER 17

BLACK TO PLAY

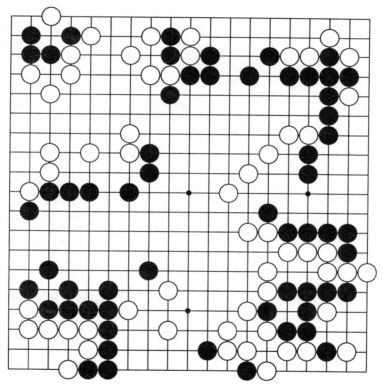

It is clear that there are lingering problems (aji) in the shape of the stones in three places: the upper right corner, the lower right corner and the lower left corner.

Where does the reader imagine is the best place for black to play?

(16% respondent success rate)

Solution

Ko in the Lower Right Corner

Solution Diagram If one looks closely at the position of the stones in the lower right corner, one realizes that black's marked stone has come to be situated in an unusual place. Actually, this one stone turns out to be the lifeline for black in the lower right.

The correct move for black is to hane at 1. If white replies at 2, black 3 makes ko. White cannot play at **a**, which demonstrates the usefulness of the marked black stone. Since the corner will be made alive if black connects at **b**, this is a direct ko. In the board position here, playing in this corner right away is the biggest move. If black plays 1 at 2, white connects underneath at **b**, and there is no problem of losing stones due to a shortage of liberties, regardless of the marked black stone.

Diagram 1 (Second best) Capturing at black 1 on the upper side is also big. With this move, white's stones in the corner are completely captured. If white plays 2, black makes the placement at 3 first and then plays 5. Next, if white hanes at **a**, black answers at **b**, and turning at white **c** is refuted by black's pushing out at **d**. If black 1 is not on the board, pushing out at black **d** would not be possible.

Diagram 2 (Ko in the lower left corner as well) If black makes the placement at 1 in the lower left corner, the moves through 5 result in ko, but compared to the situation analyzed in the **Solution Diagram**, this is too small.

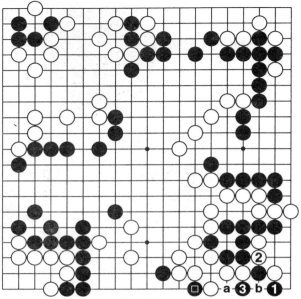

Solution Diagram

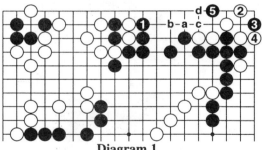

Diagram 1

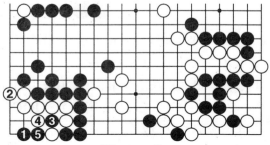

Diagram 2

The Middlegame

PROBLEM NUMBER 18

WHITE TO PLAY

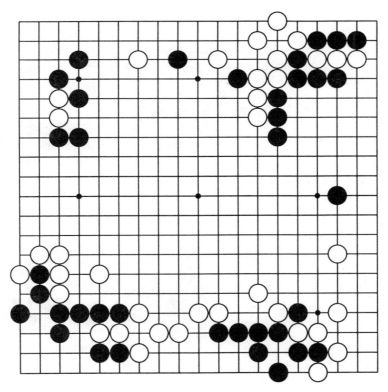

The focal point is on the lower side. There are big moves to be made on the upper side as well, but the method one can use on the lower side outranks them in terms of severity. Please read out the situation to the very end.

(20% respondent success rate)

Solution

The Shot of the Placement Move

Solution Diagram The two black groups on the lower side are each alive independently. However, if a two-pronged attack can be mustered, an opportunity will suddenly present itself.

The placement of white 1 is a severe move. With this one shot, black is faced with a serious dilemma. The upshot is that if attaches at 2, the moves through 5 result in a flower-viewing ko for white. Forcing with white **a**, black **b** first would result in the same outcome, but in that case white would have played ko threats before the fact, incurring a loss in effect.

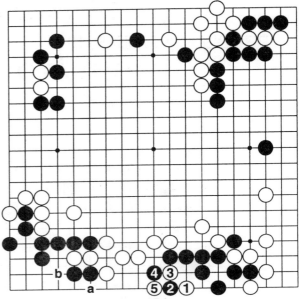

Solution Diagram

Diagram 1 (The corner becomes ko) If, in response to the placement of white 1, black responds at 2, the hane at 3 is white's pride and joy, a move that puts pressure on both black groups to the left and right. If black makes life for the group to the right with 4, with the moves from white 5 through 11, the corner becomes ko, and this would be even bigger.

Also, if white plays 3 at **a**, trying to capture black directly, then after black plays at 4, white **b**, and black **c** makes the interior space of black's group wide enough to turn the position into seki.

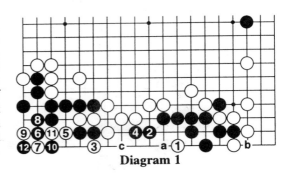

Diagram 1

Diagram 2 (Black is dead) When white hanes at 3, protecting the corner at 4 allows white to play the vital point at 5 and black is dead as a door nail. This a "worst case" scenario for black.

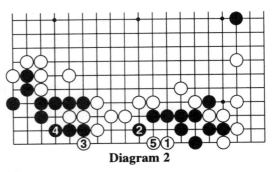

Diagram 2

42

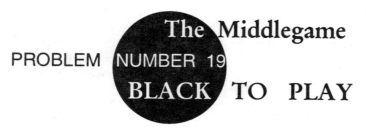

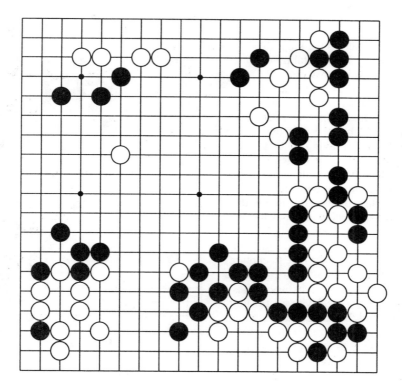

It looks as if black's stones on the upper side and on the left side are thin. One might wonder which to evaluate as the most important, but if there were an order of moves available that would take care of both sides, nothing could be better.

(7% respondent success rate)

Solution

Settle the Shape by Attaching Across the Knight's Move

Solution Diagram White's shape in the upper right is nothing to brag about. Black must consider how to play here in order to work up an attack against this white group.

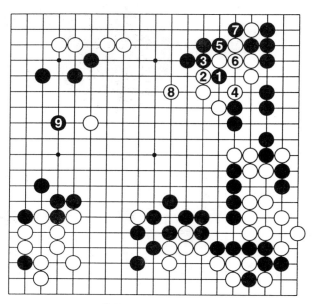

Solution Diagram

The attachment across the knight's move with black 1 is the vital point in this shape. If white answers at 2, the sequence from the cut of black 3 up to 7 is inevitable. Naturally, the profit that black makes on the upper side is not small, but the fact that white cannot omit playing at 8 is equally important. Black manages to play first on the left side with 9, and has been able to play on both sides. Of course, if white plays elsewhere with 8, the knight's move attack with black 8 would be severe.

Diagram 1 (Winning the race to capture) When black makes the attachment across the knight's move, it is necessary to have an answer prepared to deal with white's butting move at 2 and the counterattack with 4 & 6. With the moves from 9 through 25, black wins the race to capture [semeai] by one move. If white plays 16 at 24, black makes an eye at 16 and has nothing to worry about.

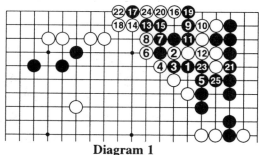

Diagram 1

Diagram 2 (White deals with the situation) Pushing out with black 1 is not sufficient to mount an effective attack. When white plays at 2, poking at black 3 will be answered by the cut of white 4, which will allow white to deal with the situation [sabaki] without any problems.

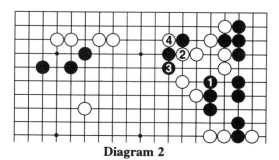

Diagram 2

44

The Middlegame

PROBLEM NUMBER 20

WHITE TO PLAY

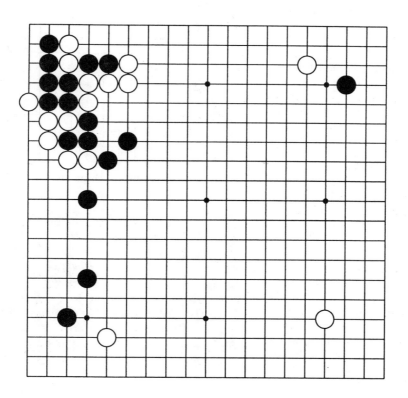

The sparring in the upper left corner has yet to come to a lull. What is best continuation for white to follow? However, keep in mind that just making defensive moves on the left side would be unsatisfactory.

(6% respondent success rate)

Solution

Play for a One Move Approach Ko

Solution Diagram White's group on the left side can not be left just as it is, but what will happen if the corner devolves to a race to capture [semeai]? That is the premise of this problem.

Tackling the situation with the descending move at white 1 is interesting. Black 2 and white 3 are natural, then when black jumps to 4, white connects with 5, and with the moves through 11 a one move approach ko favorable to white results.

During this variation, if black plays 2 at 3, white plays at 2, followed by black **a**, white **b**, and since filling liberties on either side is impossible, black is destroyed.

Diagram 1 (Black plays unreasonably) When white captures with 1 & 3, poking at black 4 is bad. White plays 5, and if black fills a liberty with 6, white wins the race to capture [semeai] in the corner with 7. If black plays 6 at **a**, white can make ko with a move at **b**, but instead of doing so, can strike across the knight's move at **c**.

Diagram 2 (White loses) If white simply plays at 1 to capture the two black stones, getting forced [kikashi] with the atari of black 2 is terrible. This time when black fills liberties with 4 & 6, after the moves through 12 a double ko results, and white is lost.

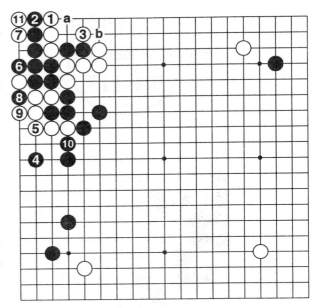

Solution Diagram

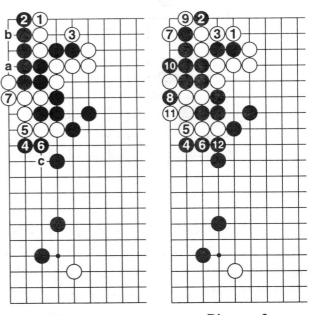

Diagram 1   **Diagram 2**

The Middlegame

PROBLEM NUMBER 21

WHITE TO PLAY

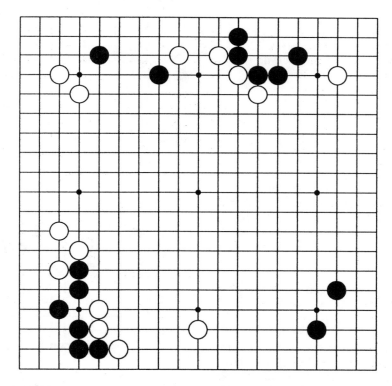

Both the white and black stones on the upper side exhibit thin shape. But merely playing defensively would give black breathing room.

What plan will allow one to take the advantage in the game at a single stroke?

(13% respondent success rate)

Solution

Settle the Shape with a Fencing in Move

Solution Diagram Concentrating solely on the question of profit and loss in a local area will not produce a chance for one to grasp a winning opportunity.

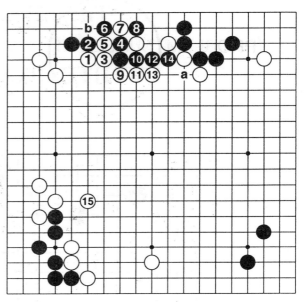

Solution Diagram

The correct answer is the fencing in move of white 1. After black 2, white plays 3, but when black descends to 4, it may seem like white is stymied. However, it is essential to intuitively sense that the white stones on the upper side are light and easily expendable. After pushing through and cutting with white 5 & 7, the moves following 9 settle the shape, and after playing at 15, white develops a magnificent territorial framework [moyo] in the center. After this, in regards to the upper side, white can still connect at **a**, and is left with the big move at **b** which allows white to capture two black stones.

During this sequence, if black plays 2 at 4, white 2 takes sufficient profit and white can feel satisfied.

Diagram 1 (Sufficient for black) Commencing operations by shoring up white's thin position with 1 results in black having an easy time of it. When black plays at 2, white cannot neglect defending at 3, and then playing at 4 gives black a sufficient result.

Diagram 2 (Much the same) Pressing underneath with white 1 turns out the same way, with black dodging the attack [sabaki] with 2 & 4.

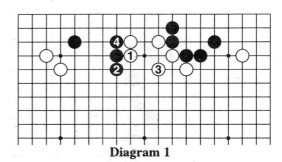

Diagram 1

Diagram 2

48

The Middlegame

PROBLEM NUMBER 22

WHITE TO PLAY

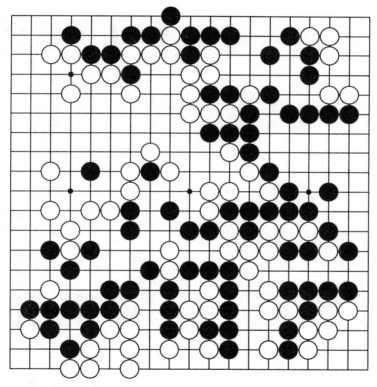

If one simply applies an acute attention span, this is an elementary problem.

But even though one's attention may be directed correctly, if one plays in such a way as to make a loss, a correct solution cannot be imagined.

(11% respondent success rate)

Solution

Defend the Lower Side

Solution Diagram In the middle-game, the most important factor is the life and death of groups of stones. If one misjudges such a situation, all of one's efforts up to then go up in smoke.

In this board position white's group on the lower side is still not completely safe. Naturally, protecting this group is the top priority. Starting with the move in the corner at white 1 is correct here. If black plays 2 & 4, preventing white from making another eye, then white lives with 5. Playing white 1 simply at 5 or at **a** would leave black with the opportunity to capture at 3 afterward, and therefore represent a loss for white. That would be inferior to the variation given.

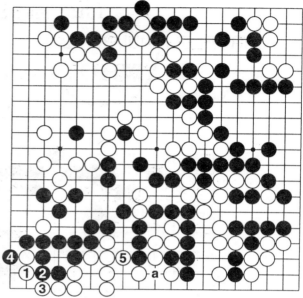

Solution Diagram

Diagram 1 (A large ko) Leaving the lower side as it is to play elsewhere would be terrible for white. Descending to 1 gives black equally attractive continuations [miai] on the left and the right. If white responds by protecting the group to the right with 2, black attaches at 3, and with the moves through 7, a ko results. Of course, if white defends the group to the left with the move at 2, black plays at **a**, capturing twelve of white's stones.

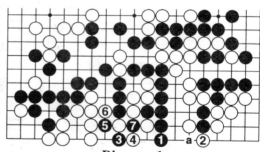

Diagram 1

Diagram 2 (Small) Blocking at white 1 in the upper left corner is not as big as it looks. If, on the contrary, black plays at 1, a white move at **a** leaves white with the option of playing **b**, black **c** and white **d** later. Also, black **e** in the upper right makes ko, but that is too small at this point.

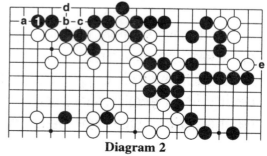

Diagram 2

50

The Middlegame

PROBLEM NUMBER 23

BLACK TO PLAY

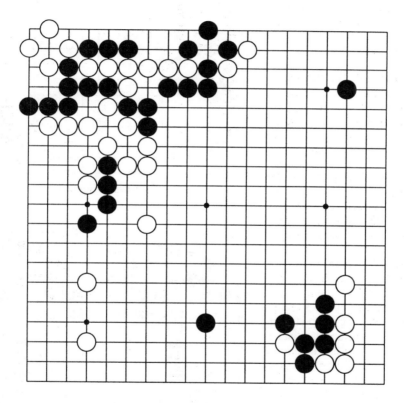

A violent confrontation in the upper left corner has come to a pause. Well then, the problem to be faced in the present situation is the disposition of the four black stones on the left side, but what kind of plan should be considered? Just running out would be bad.

(10% respondent success rate)

Solution

An Attachment Deals with the Problem [Sabaki]

Solution Diagram If black simply runs out into the center with the four stones on the left side, there is nothing pleasant to look forward to. When one considers the best thing to do, one tends to lean toward sacrificing the stones.

With that in mind, the attachment of black 1, probing white's response, is a skillful way to deal with the problem [sabaki]. If white answers at 2, black eats into the corner with 3, and after white 4 & 6, black connects at 7. After that, even if white attacks with 10, the continuation through 25 can be predicted, and if white's territory ends up being disrupted to this extent, black can feel greatly satisfied to be left with a living group.

Diagram 1 (Unreasonable for white) When black attaches at 1, the hane outward of white 2 will be met with the cross-cut of black 3 and attachment of 5, playing in good form. According to circumstances, black is fully resolved to sacrifice the stones on the left side. If white plays in an uncompromising manner with 6 and the following, up to black 23, white merely compounds the damage.

Diagram 2 (Heavy) The jumping attachment of black 1 and hane of 3 is a common sense way to deal with the stones [sabaki], but it is somewhat heavy. White defends the corner through 8, and even after black jumps to 9, the group is still not alive.

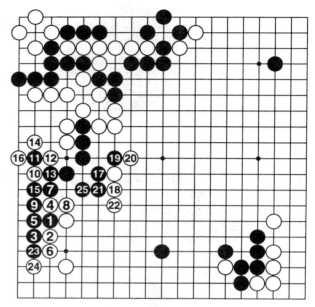

Solution Diagram

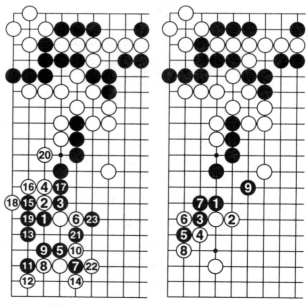

Diagram 1   **Diagram 2**

52

The Middlegame

PROBLEM NUMBER 24

BLACK TO PLAY

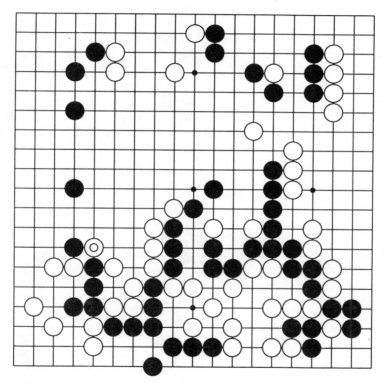

The cut with the marked white stone has just been played. If the marked white stone, or else the white stones in the center can be captured, that would be the very best thing to do. However, if that cannot be accomplished, what would be the best way to play?

(11% respondent success rate)

Solution

Wrap the Opponent up on a Grand Scale

Solution Diagram White's stones in the center cannot be captured. If black tries to do so unreasonably, black's four stones have already been captured so it will only compound black's loss. Such being the case, the problem becomes one of finding a way to wrap white's stones up. Throwing the stone in at black 1 is the best thing to do. Forcing white to capture with 2 eliminates one of white's liberties. This one liberty plays an important role in the wrapping up operation to come.

Black sets the shape with the atari of 3, and then forcing [kikashi] with 5 is the correct order of moves. There are potential problems [aji] in this corner, so white has no choice but to play 6 & 8. Then, when black cuts at 11, white struggles mightily to push out with the moves from 12 to 30. But up to 33, black is successful in wrapping white up on a grand scale. If, instead of playing at 1, black had played atari at 3, white would connect at 4; also, black 1 played as a cut at 11 would be answered by the connection at white 4, and in both cases, possibilities are eliminated [aji keshi], so the wrapping up operation would be less than perfect.

Diagram 1 (Unreasonable for black) It is unreasonable for black to try to capture white with the cut at 1. White easily escapes with the moves through 10. Now there is no wrapping white up in any way.

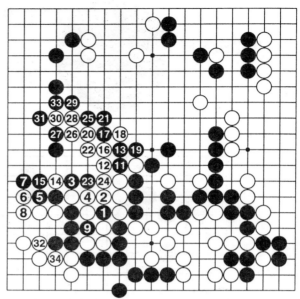

Solution Diagram 10 connects at 1

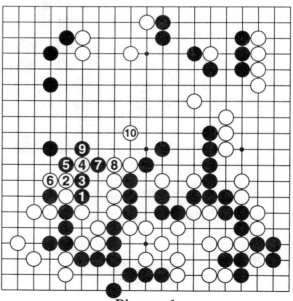

Diagram 1

54

The Middlegame

PROBLEM NUMBER 25

WHITE TO PLAY

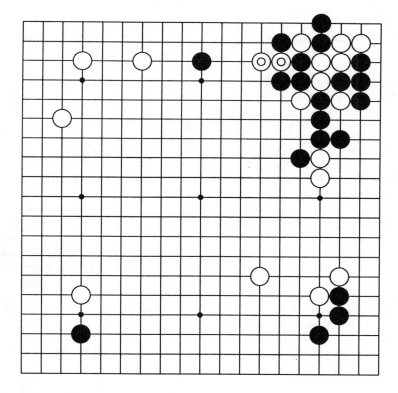

The focal point is on the upper side.

Simply running out with the two marked white stones is not an attractive option. The key is to find a way to use the captured stones in the corner to make effective forcing moves to improve white's position.

(11% respondent success rate)

Solution

Attaching on Top is the Vital Point

Solution Diagram It is wrong to use forcing moves [kikashi] against the corner, settling the shape, before knowing *which* forcing moves are most effective. An atari or a squeeze play can always be made here, so leaving the play for later is the best policy.

The correct move here is to attach directly on top of black's stone with white 1. According to how black responds with this stone, white will determine the proper way to set the shape in the corner with forcing moves. If black extends to 2, this is now the right time to set the shape in the corner with white 3 & 5, then block at 7. When play proceeds like this, blacks two stones are heavy, and will find it difficult to maneuver [sabaki].

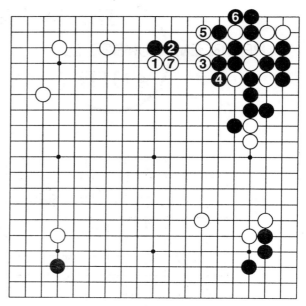

Solution Diagram

Diagram 1 (A variation) When white attaches at 1, if black hanes at 2, the crosscut of white 3 is a good move. If black extends to 4, this time white plays atari at 5, and after playing the moves through 11, a disadvantage for white cannot be imagined. Please confirm the fact that during this sequence no move besides black 4 works any better.

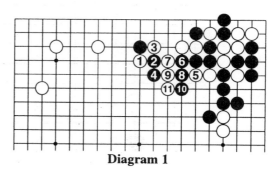

Diagram 1

Diagram 2 (Too easygoing) The jumping attachment of white 1 is sometimes good form, but when black extends to 2, white does not have a good follow-up move. White might try to lean on black's stones with 3, but black will simply defend at 4. Play proceeds to black 8, after which both sides will fight on equal footing.

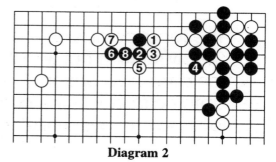

Diagram 2

56

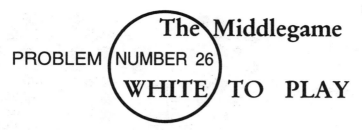

The Middlegame
PROBLEM NUMBER 26
WHITE TO PLAY

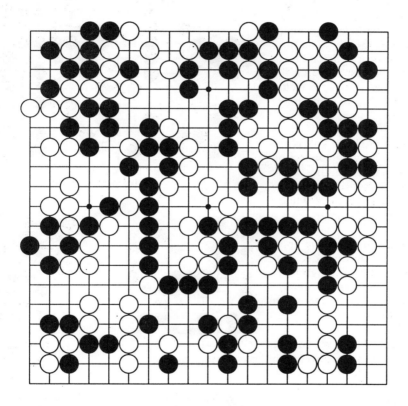

There are various areas around the board where trouble (aji) appears likely to develop.

Where and what moves exist in this position? First of all, examine the situation thoroughly. Without doing so, one cannot come to a conclusion about the move to play.

(18% respondent success rate)

Solution

Prevent a Large Ko from Developing

Solution Diagram The correct answer is to play in the upper right corner. With the move at 1, white secures the corner without any question. If some kind of play develops in this corner, white's large group of stones are put in danger, so no matter how one looks at it, defending at white 1 is the biggest move on the board. White 1 at **a**, **b**, or **c** would also be correct. But if white plays elsewhere here...

Diagram 1 (A large ko) When black plays the hanging connection of 1, white is in trouble. After white plays 4, black 5 starts a large ko on which the life and death of white's large group of stones hinges.

Diagram 2 (Small) In the upper left corner, white has a move with the attachment of 1. Through black 6, a ko results, but this is obviously a much smaller move than the one in the **Solution Diagram**.

Diagram 3 (A one move win) There is no play in the lower right corner. Black 1 is the proper form to use to try to create play in the corner, but white replies with 2 through 8, winning the race to capture [semeai] by one move.

Diagram 4 (Black is dead) In the lower left corner, black might try to play the move at 1, but through white 8, black ends up unconditionally dead.

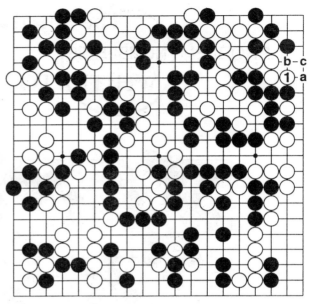

Solution Diagram

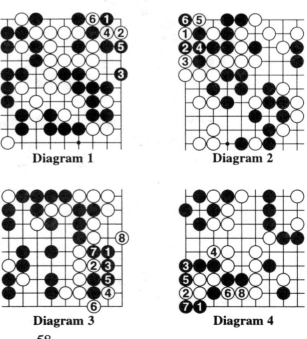

Diagram 1

Diagram 2

Diagram 3

Diagram 4

58

The Middlegame

PROBLEM NUMBER 27

BLACK TO PLAY

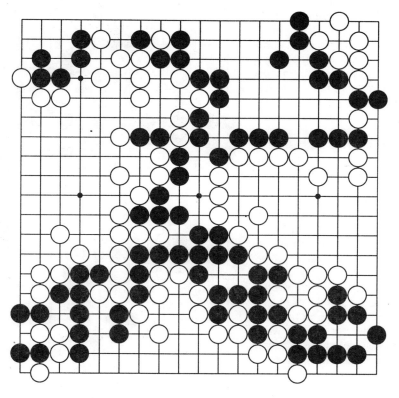

Black's connection with the large group of stones in the center is still not clearly established.

Should black expend a move in the center, or is there another method that can be used elsewhere in place of that? There lies the crux of the matter.

(8% respondent success rate)

Solution

Two Birds with One Stone

Solution Diagram White can play at **a**, black **b**, white **c**, black **d**, and white **e**, making the connection of black's large central black group with the upper side and its life itself dependent upon the outcome of this large scale ko. Therefore, black might be tempted to play at **c**, eliminating this possibility for the sake of peace of mind. However, before doing that, one wants to probe white's lower side, since finding a move there would be a better solution.

Cutting at black 1 is the best move here. White 2 is the only response, and then cutting at black 3 is good form. If white plays 4, black 5 & 7 capture two stones. The upshot is that black has not only managed to ruin white's territory on the lower side, but to make a connection with the upper side unnecessary.

In addition, if white plays elsewhere after this, the poke of black **f** is a big move. White **g** in response would invite black **h**, leaving white dead, so white would have to play at **g**. That leaves black with the move at **g**, capturing several stones.

Diagram 1 (Winning the ko) After the black cut at 1 and extension to 5, it is unreasonable for white to atari from above with 6, and then play 8 & 10. When white takes ko with 16, black has a lifeline in the capture at 17, and when white takes with 18, black 19 forces white to back down with 20.

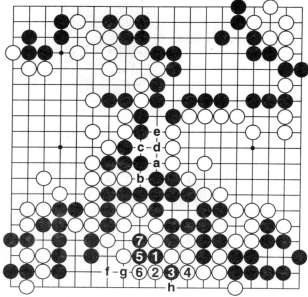

Solution Diagram

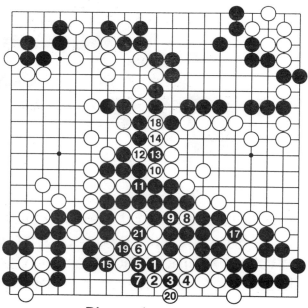

Diagram 1   16 takes ko at 12

The Middlegame

PROBLEM NUMBER 28

WHITE TO PLAY

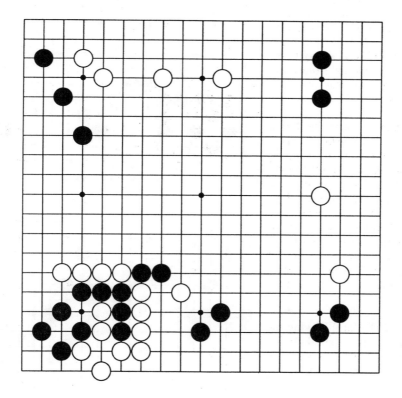

No hint this time.
There is an absolutely decisive blow to play here.

(44% respondent success rate)

Solution

Capture the Pivotal Stones

Solution Diagram The board position depicted here is still in the opening stage of the game, but in the lower left area, black's two marked stones separate white's groups of stones on the left and lower sides, limiting white's freedom of movement. Usually, a strong way of playing would be to devise a way to attack black's two marked stones, but in this situation that way of thinking is no good.

The attachment of white 1 is a powerful shot. This one move solves all of white's problems. Black has no choice but to capture with the move at 2, so white is able to capture five black stones with the move at 3. Taking these pivotal stones means that the value of black's two marked stones is for all intents and purposes nullified. It goes without saying that if black plays 2 at 3, white plays at 2 and black's stones are dead as they sit.

Diagram 1 (Failure) Playing the atari of white 1 is no good. When black plays at 2, white 3 allows black to capture two stones with 4, living easily.

Diagram 2 (A good point, but) The checking extension of white 1 occupies a good point to attack black in the upper left, but black defends the corner with 2, and white 3 is answered by black 4. As before, white's shape is split in two, but now there is no remedy for it.

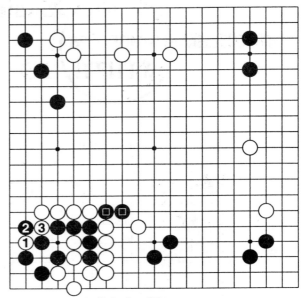

Solution Diagram

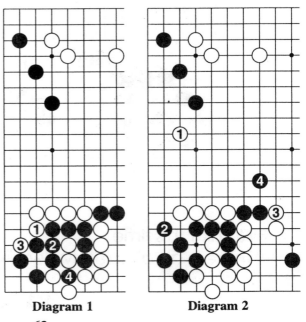

Diagram 1   **Diagram 2**

62

The Middlegame

PROBLEM NUMBER 29

WHITE TO PLAY

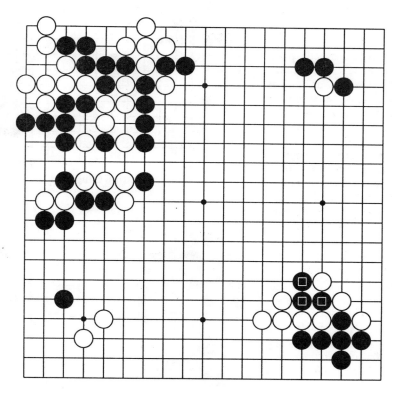

A complicated position in the upper left has resulted from a violent fight there. Naturally, the focus here is on where a winning play can be made, but the relationship between black's three marked stones and the ladder must not be overlooked.

(48% respondent success rate)

Solution

A Perfect Ladder Break

Solution Diagram First, it is necessary to thoroughly analyze the position of the stones in the upper left. If white wants to merely run out into the center, it is a simple matter, but if possible, white would also like to rescue the two marked stones.

In that case, white bluntly pokes with the move at 1, a ladder break. This causes black serious difficulties. When black avoids the ladder by playing at 2, white plays at 3, then cuts at 5 and fights. After black 6, white plays at 7, and next, moves at either **a** or **b** are equivalent options [miai] for white. After this, if black plays at **c**, white captures at **b**; now if black plays at **d**, white has an escape prepared at **e**, and white's move at 1 demonstrates its effectiveness.

An attachment with white 1 at **f** would have the same meaning, and would also be correct.

Diagram 1 (White loses the race to capture) Directly playing atari at white 1 and cutting at 3 fails to take into account that the circumstances are completely different. When black turns at 6, even if white fills in a liberty with 7, black wins the race to capture [semeai] with 8. After this, if white pokes at **a**, much more is at stake in this area, so it is too short-sighted to expect black to respond at **b**. Instead, black will connect at **c**, and when white captures black's stones in a ladder at **b**, black plays at **d**, and black's left side is very big.

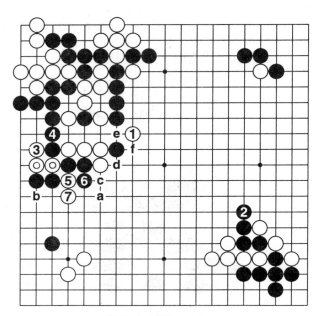

Solution Diagram

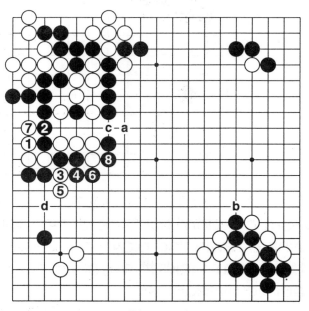

Diagram 1

64

The Middlegame

PROBLEM NUMBER 30

BLACK TO PLAY

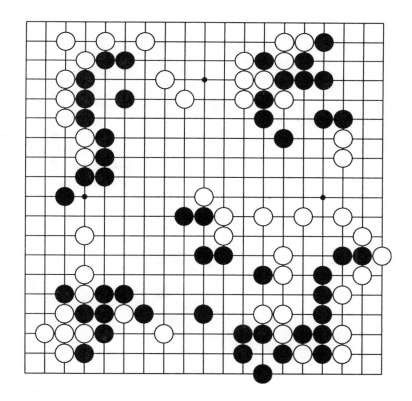

At length, the middlegame has come to its closing stages. Where is the biggest move for black to play? The focal point is on the left side.

(37% respondent success rate)

Solution

After Wedging in, Cut

Solution Diagram Here, the life and death of stones has been clearly established; the next best thing to do is to look for stones somewhere that can be forcibly ripped away from the opponent and captured.

Wedging in with black 1 on the left side is a severe technique. This one move severs white's connection with the marked stone. If white plays atari from below with 2, black extends to 3, and when white plays 4, black cuts at 5. Black secures a significant amount of territory at a single stroke.

If white plays 2 from above as an atari at 3, black extends to 2, and next a black move at 4 or a cut at **a** are equivalent options [miai], making this the worst case scenario for white. If white plays 2 defensively at 4, black extends to 3 and again the marked white stone is cut off.

Diagram 1 (Sliding in) If one is not aware of the wedging in move in the **Solution Diagram**, one will likely slide in with black 1. If white defends at 2, poking at **a** gives black a good initiative. Even if white defends with 2 at **b**, black can likewise play at **a**.

Diagram 2 (Poking) Poking from below with black 1 is unappealing. White makes thickness in the center with 2 & 4, bringing black's moves into question. If black now plays **a**, white plays **b**, and no connection for black is possible.

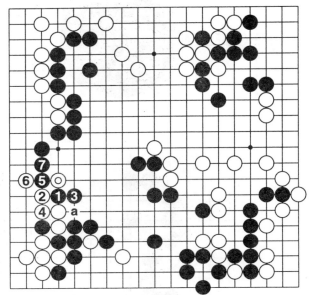

Solution Diagram

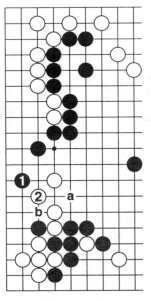

Diagram 1

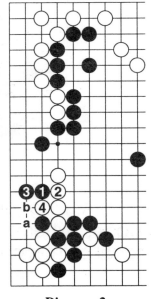

Diagram 2

The Middlegame

PROBLEM NUMBER 31

WHITE TO PLAY

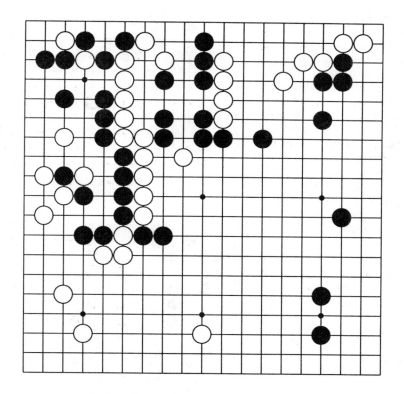

The urgent requirement in the present situation is the safekeeping (shinogi) of the large group of white stones extending from the upper side into the center. How should white play here? The query is made concerning how to best safeguard (shinogi) these stones.

(44% respondent success rate)

Solution

Land a Solid Blow with an Attachment

Solution Diagram If one dawdles at this stage of the game, there is no chance to win. The correct answer is to play the attachment of white 1. One could not ask for a more ideal vital point to play; black's two stones are completely immobilized by this move. The point of the matter is that if black tries to move out with these stones unreasonably, the damage that black sustains will be that much greater. Consequently, the capping move of black 2 is par for the situation, but white captures black's stones cleanly with 3 and has no worries. Furthermore, when this group in the center becomes strong in this way, white can invade black's large territorial framework [moyo] on the right side without restraints.

Playing a capping move with white 1 at **a** would be slack, making too loose shape. If black immediately moves out with **b**, it will be difficult for white, while black also has the option of dodging to play at 2, and there is no move for white to cleanly capture black's two stones above.

Diagram 1 (Unreasonable for black) When white attaches at 1, moving out with black 2 is unreasonable. White's counter-hane of 3 is strong, and when black counterattacks with 4 & 6, white plays 7 through 15. Once black's connection has been severed, in the coming race to capture [semeai] black will be unable to find more liberties.

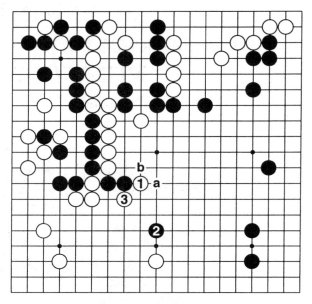

Solution Diagram

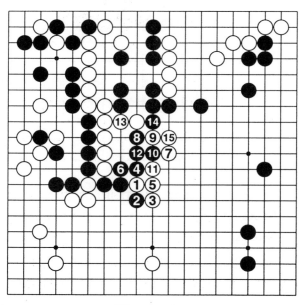

Diagram 1

68

Perception
PROBLEM NUMBER 32
WHITE TO PLAY

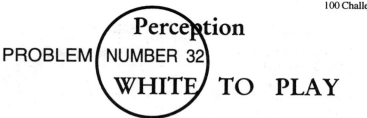

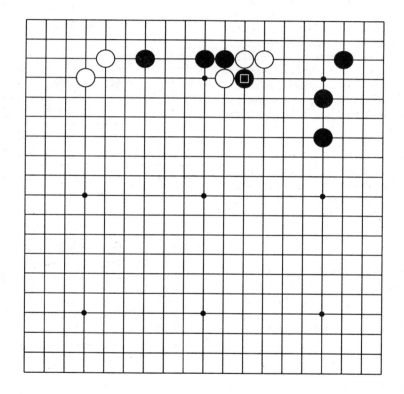

Black has just cut with the marked stone. It will not go well if white tries to capture this stone directly.

There is a go proverb that states that if one's real intent is to play on the left, feint to the right.

(13% respondent success rate)

Solution

Play an Attachment that is Effective on Both Sides

Solution Diagram The attachment of white 1 is the only move. Black is rocked by the blow from this attachment and is hard pressed to come up with an answer. The long and short of the matter is that if black defends by blocking at 2, white plays atari at 3 and the following moves, and after playing white 11, taking one stone at **a** and capturing at **b** are equivalent options [miai] for white. However, if black plays 2 as an extension at 3, defending the group to the left, white will push through at 2, getting a sufficient result.

Diagram 1 (Insufficiently forceful) White 1 is a similar attachment, but it is too easygoing. Black extends to 2, and even if white attacks on the right side at 3 & 5, the connection of black 6 leaves white without a follow-up move.

Diagram 2 (Sufficient for black) In response to the poke of white 1, black will likewise extend at 2 here, and the result of the variation through white 9 is that black takes a large territory on the upper side of the board.

Diagram 3 (A big loss) Analyzing the situation where white plays atari at 1 & 3 right away: if white cannot capture these black stones, then playing this way violates the general principle of not incurring a loss in advance of seeking profit. Even though white gets to burst into black's position with the move at 9, the question of the disposition of the corner has already become a minor consideration.

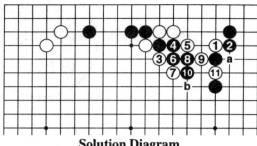

Solution Diagram

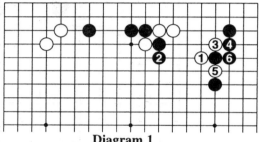

Diagram 1

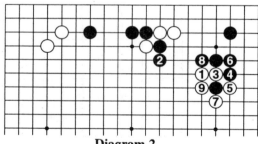

Diagram 2

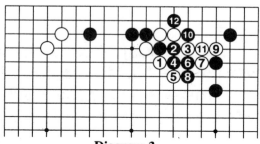

Diagram 3

70

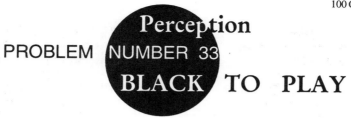

Perception
PROBLEM NUMBER 33
BLACK TO PLAY

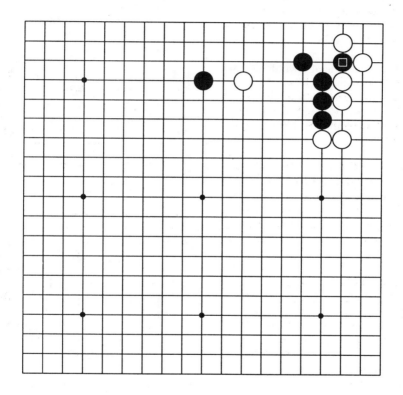

It would not show much skill if, in answer to the atari on the marked stone, black just connects.

Now is the chance to make a preventative strike against the defects in white's shape to get the jump on white.

(8% respondent success rate)

Solution

Lean on One Side to Attack on the Other Side

Solution Diagram Pushing through at black 1 and cutting at 3 is a severe measure that beats white down. When white connects at 4, black leans on white's position while attacking with the move at 5, and this is a natural way of bringing white's marked stone under attack as well.

Playing black 3 as a cut at 4 would lead to the variation with white **a**, black 3, white **b**, and black 5. This seems to be the same result as in the previous diagram, but to the extent that white's position is solidified, this is a loss for black.

Diagram 1 (Lacking forcefulness) If, after pushing through once with 1, black connects at 3, white also connects at 4 and black is badly off. This time the hane of black 5 lacks severity since black has not inserted the cut at **a**, so white is given leeway to run away at **b**.

Diagram 2 (Black is badly off) Simply pushing through with black 1 and then playing hane at 3 invites white to capture one stone with the move at 4, and black is plagued with a shortage of liberties. Black is in miserable shape here. Rather than suffer such a fate, it would be better to just play hane at black 3 without pushing through first at 1.

Diagram 3 (Unreasonable maneuvers) If black tries to attack white's stone directly with 1, white moves out with 2 & 4, and black's maneuver is shown to be unreasonable. Black 1 at 2 would be answered by white **a**, and the result is more or less the same.

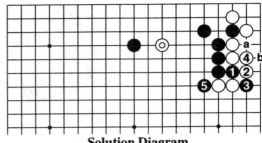

Solution Diagram

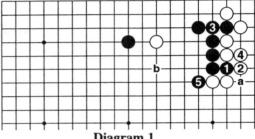

Diagram 1

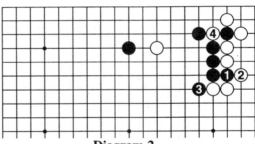

Diagram 2

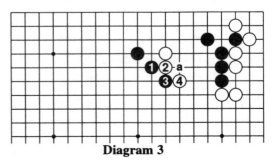

Diagram 3

Perception
PROBLEM NUMBER 34
BLACK TO PLAY

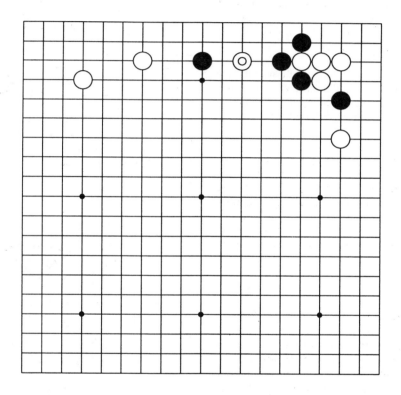

At this point, white has invaded with the marked stone. Well then, how can black's stones be stabilized (sabaki) in this situation? This is a position that calls for an intuitive grasp of the pluses and minuses in order to make the next move.

(9% respondent success rate)

Solution

A Simple Attachment is Good Form

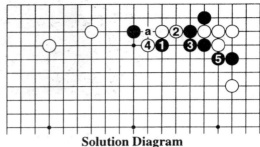

Solution Diagram

Solution Diagram Attaching at black 1 to see how white reacts is a skillful finesse [tesuji] that shows good intuition. If white responds by butting against black's position with 2, black gets the impetus to connect at 3, making black 5 or a move at 4 equivalent options [miai] for black.

Instead of playing at 2, white might hane outward at 4, but in that case as well, black would connect at 3, making black 5 and the cut at **a** equally attractive alternatives [miai].

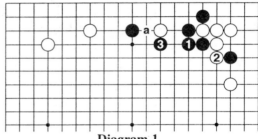

Diagram 1

Diagram 1 (Forfeiting possible alternatives) Connecting first at black 1 allows white to defend at 2, and black has forfeited the possible alternatives [aji keshi] that once were here. Then when black attaches at 3, white is left with other options that are painful for black to contemplate, such as butting against black's stone with a move at white **a**.

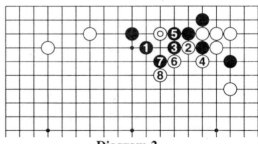

Diagram 2

Diagram 2 (White makes good shape) Playing the diagonal move of black 1 in the expectation that white will run out with the marked stone is not good. White will instead blithely discard it to capture a stone with 2 & 4. Black can do nothing but suffer in silence.

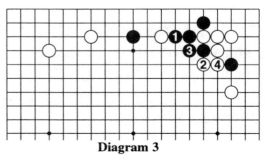

Diagram 3

Diagram 3 (Bad shape) If black butts stiffly against white's stone with 1, here too white will shun putting the stone into motion. White 2 & 4 are calm and collected moves that turn black's move at 1 into the bad shape of an empty triangle.

Perception

PROBLEM NUMBER 35

BLACK TO PLAY

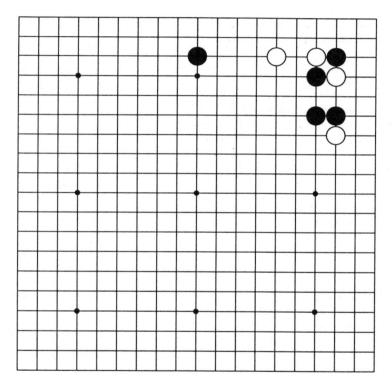

·White has presently cross-cut in the corner. One must decide what move to make based upon one's judgment of which stones to view as most important in this situation.

Intuition should be brought to bear on the question of how to make white heavy and vulnerable to attack.

(10% respondent success rate)

Solution

Combine Attack and Defense

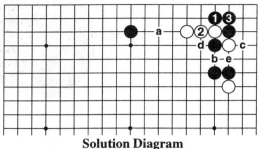

Solution Diagram

Solution Diagram The atari of black 1 and the connection of 3 make white's stones heavy and the object of attack while also defending black's own group, so these are moves that combine both attack and defense. After this, a checking extension of white **a** is par for this situation, but black will aim at attacking this group for some time to come.

In addition, if white plays atari at **b**, the sequence continues with black **c**, white **d**, and black **e**, and black has no cause for dissatisfaction. Here white would prefer to aim at the possibility [aji] of descending to **c**.

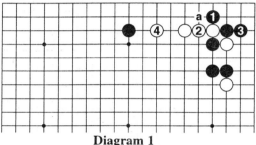

Diagram 1

Diagram 1 (Insufficient for attacking) After the atari of black 1, the descending move at 3 exhibits good form, but its defect is that it leaves the block of **a** at white's disposal. Considering the ways in which the white stones can be attacked, this variation drops a degree in severity.

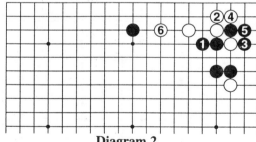

Diagram 2

Diagram 2 (Black is dissatisfied) If black extends to 1, white 2 threatens the black corner. Since black cannot omit playing at 3, white gets the opportunity to play at 4 & 6, settling the group. Also, if black uses the move at 1 to simply clasp hold of white's stone by playing at 3, white plays atari at 1, forcing black's stones into overconcentration [kori-gatachi].

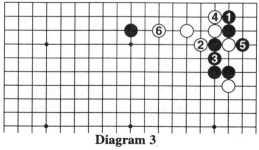

Diagram 3

Diagram 3 (Sufficient for white) Descending to black 1 in the corner would not only invite white to atari at 2, but also play the forcing move [kikashi] at 4, and this is a sufficient result for white.

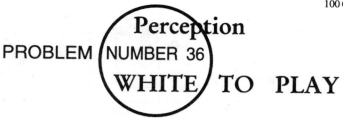

Perception

PROBLEM NUMBER 36

WHITE TO PLAY

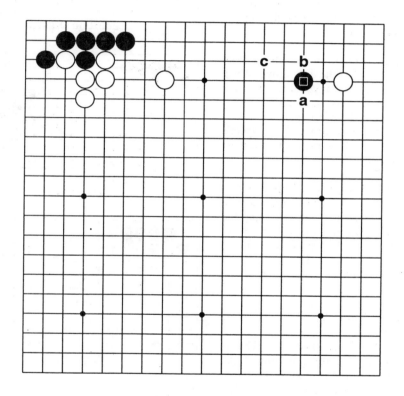

Black has attacked the corner with the marked stone. Among the choices of moves at **a, b** and **c**, which should white play?

Of course, the disposition of the stones in the upper left must be taken into consideration.

(41% respondent success rate)

Solution

Attaching from Above is Best

Solution Diagram Deciding which joseki to use is not only a question to be answered by the conditions in the local area in which it will be played. According to the distribution of stones in the surrounding area, the same joseki might be either a good one or a bad one to play.

In this board position, attaching from above with white 1 is the only move. When black hanes at 2, the moves through white 7 are joseki, but please notice that the result is that the influence that black develops in this area is mitigated by white's marked stone, which jumps out to erase the potential of black's stones.

Diagram 1 (A variation) Depending on conditions in the lower right corner, at 5 in the previous diagram, white may play the more forceful two-step hane of 1 & 3 here. At the point of 8, if black plays hane, white cuts at 9, and it cannot be imagined that in this fight white will be at a disadvantage.

Diagram 2 (A mistaken choice) If white attaches from below with 1, sliding down with black 2 & 4 works just right. That is because considering the position of the marked white and black stones, the upper side is not an area that black views as being important.

Diagram 3 (White is too easygoing) Playing the pincer of white 1 also is wrong, since it is played from the wrong direction. When black plays the diagonal move of 2, white's stones on the upper side are found to be placed in a manner that is too easygoing.

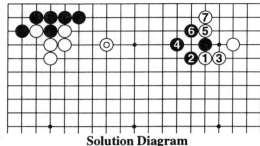

Solution Diagram

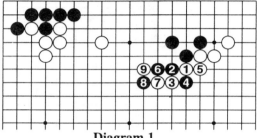

Diagram 1

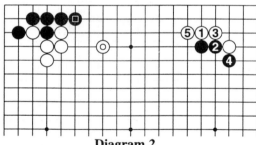

Diagram 2

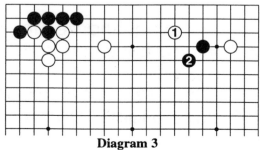

Diagram 3

78

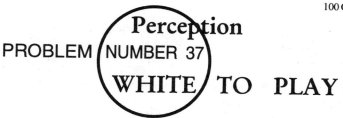

Perception

PROBLEM NUMBER 37

WHITE TO PLAY

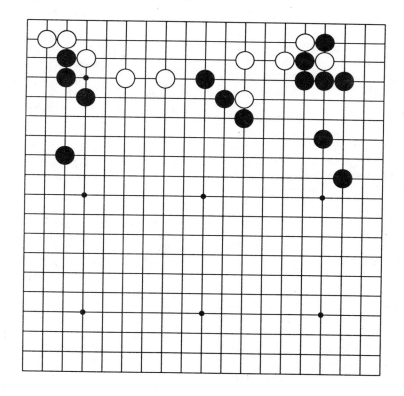

How should white play on the upper side?
Determining intuitively the good and bad aspects of this position will greatly influence how matters develop and are handled afterwards.

(32% respondent success rate)

Solution

Connect by Means of an Attachment

Solution Diagram If white can connect the groups of stones to the left and right on the upper side together nothing could be better.

The solution is to make the attachment of white 1. With this move white accomplishes the goal spelled out above without any difficulty. If black responds at 2, white connects at 3, and white's position is completely safe and sound.

Diagram 1 (Black plays unreasonably) The hane into white's position of black 1 is a counterattack which is natural to envision. However, white fights back by wedging into black's position with 3, and cutting with 5, showing up black's play as being unreasonable. With the moves following 8, black thrashes around within white's position, but when white hanes at 17, it is clear that black is at a disadvantage in the race to capture [semeai] here.

Diagram 2 (Split shape) The wedging move of white 1 seems like good form, but it is painful to be forced [kikashi] with the atari of black 2. Even if white later cuts at 5, black 6 & 8 press white hard. In the end, white is forced into a one-sided defensive battle.

Diagram 3 (White in agony) The white connection of 1 would be met by black 2, cutting the link between white's two positions. After this, white **a** is answered by black **b**, and white will go through agony trying to devise a way to escape.

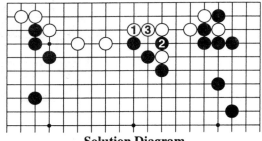

Solution Diagram

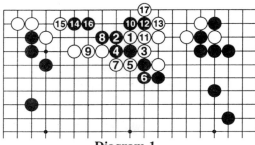

Diagram 1

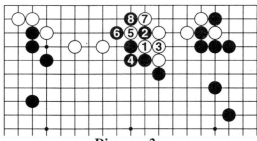

Diagram 2

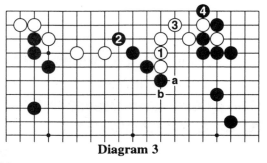

Diagram 3

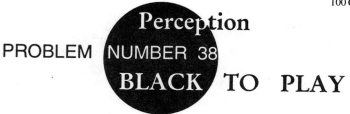

Perception
PROBLEM NUMBER 38
BLACK TO PLAY

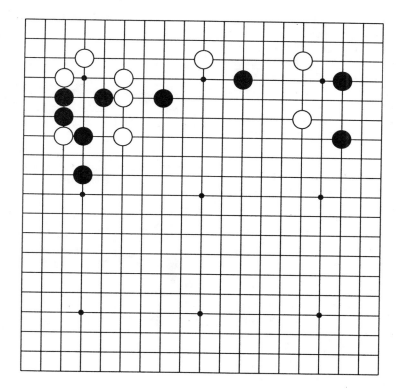

The shape on the upper side is all too vaguely sketched out. But where is the best place for black to begin operations to settle the shape?

Playing so as to leave the most possibilities and nuances to aim at is the most effective way.

(26% respondent success rate)

Solution

Fix the Shape with an Attachment

Solution Diagram Black attaches at 1 to see what will happen. Black's strategy is to determine how to play on the right according to how white responds here.

If white counterattacks with 2, black cuts at 3 and fights white head on. After white plays 12, black appears to be in an excruciatingly difficult position, but black's aim all along has been to cut with the moves from 13 through 17, and has ample resources to fight here. For white's part, the prospect of a black hane at **a** and a descending move at black **b** is enough to cause a nervous breakdown.

Diagram 1 (Heavy maneuvering) Playing black 1 & 3 ahead of time eliminates options [aji keshi] that black had available previously. When black attaches at 5 after this, white's marked stone is less restricted in its movement since the shape to the right has already been fixed.

Diagram 2 (Forceful but...) The knight's move of black 1 can at times be forcefully deployed, but after white defends at 2 here, it is seen to be questionable. When black attaches at 3, it is obvious that the move's severity has been half negated.

Diagram 3 (White makes good shape) Black 1 & 3 are even worse moves. White is given the chance to make good shape with the moves through 6, which then makes black's job of taking care of the stones [sabaki] on the upper side that much more painfully difficult.

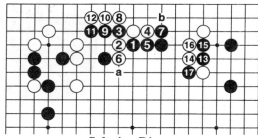

Solution Diagram

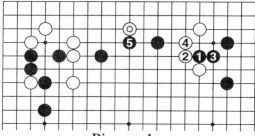

Diagram 1

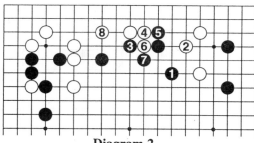

Diagram 2

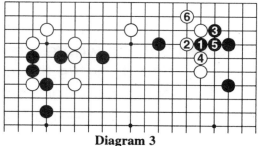

Diagram 3

Sabaki [Fancy Footwork]

PROBLEM NUMBER 39

BLACK TO PLAY

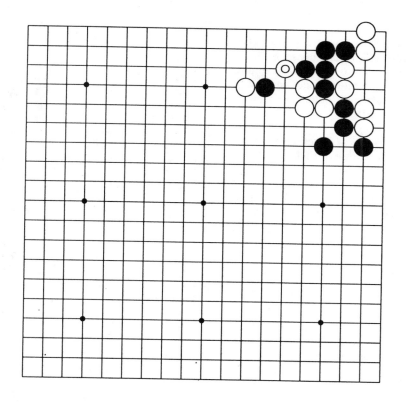

White has just played the hane with the marked stone. How does black handle (sabaki) this?

It is not good enough just to make these stones alive somehow or other. A timely sacrifice of stones may be necessary. In that case, what is the best way to do that?

(17% respondent success rate)

83

Solution

Sacrifice Stones Lightly, Easily and Shrewdly

Solution Diagram If black does not adopt a policy of sacrificing the five stones at the top here, there will be no way to deal with the situation successfully [sabaki].

First black pushes through with 1; when white answers at 2, black cuts at 3. This is the proper order of moves. If white captures at 4, black seals white's stones in with 5, and this is a sufficient outcome as far as black is concerned.

If white plays 4 at **a**, black replies at 5, and then the variation with white 4, black **b** ends up incurring a loss for white.

Diagram 1 (Insufficient) Blocking at black 3 invites white to connect at 4, leaving black badly off. When black plays at 5, white 6, or else **a**, allows white to move out into the center, and the value of black's five sacrifice stones has been cut in half.

Diagram 2 (Poorly dealing with the situation) Cutting directly with black 1 will encounter resistance with white 2. After this, if black fences white's stones in with a move at **a**, white captures the five black stones with **b**, and this way of dealing with the situation [sabaki] is inferior to the one given in the **Solution Diagram**.

Diagram 3 (Living is bad) With the moves from black 1 through 7, two eyes can be made for this group. However, black would merely make life here. It is obvious that the thickness that white makes in the process is superior.

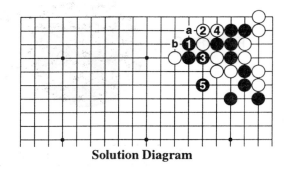

Solution Diagram

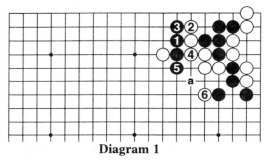

Diagram 1

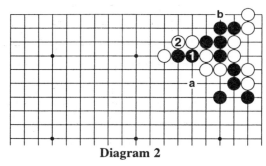

Diagram 2

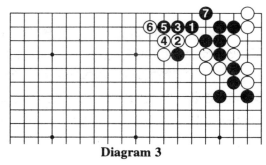

Diagram 3

84

Sabaki [Fancy Footwork]

PROBLEM NUMBER 40

WHITE TO PLAY

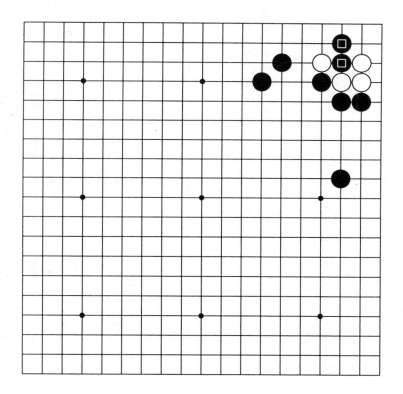

If white cannot capture the two marked black stones, there is no way to handle the situation (sabaki). Although at first sight the situation seems hopeless, the power of skillful finesse (tesuji) can be astounding. By using the correct order of moves, a brilliant sequence to make life is at hand.

(25% respondent success rate)

85

Solution

Make Life for the Stones Unconditionally

Solution Diagram Trying to capture black's two marked stones directly is unreasonable. In that case, attacking from the rear with white 1 is a common ploy in go. After the two-step hane with white 3 & 5, the moves that follow at 7 & 9 successfully carry to completion white's preparatory squeeze operation. Then white blocks at with the move at 11, and in reply to black 12, white hanes at 13, winning the race to capture [semeai] in the corner. White's play has culminated in the unconditional life of the stones here.

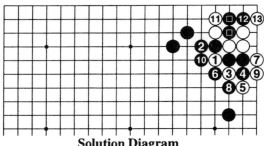

Solution Diagram

Diagram 1 (Shallow reading) Playing a single hane at white 1 and then trying to capture with the moves at 3 & 5 is reckless. Black throws in a sacrifice stone at 6 and then plays atari at 8, leaving white completely helpless.

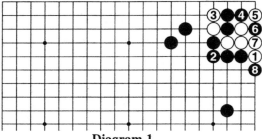

Diagram 1

Diagram 2 (Playing without a plan) If white plays atari at 1 and connects at 3, the only thing accomplished is the rescue of a single stone. However, running away with such heavy stones is the antithesis of light and easy maneuvering [sabaki], and these stones will be a concern for black for the foreseeable future.

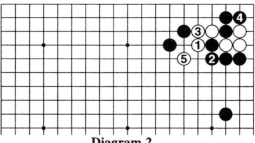

Diagram 2

Diagram 3 (Intuitive play but...) The attachment of white 1 is a move that is often an effective technique, but black will respond with the move at 2, eliminating any potential problems [aji] that may crop up here once and for all, and black has no follow-up move to play.

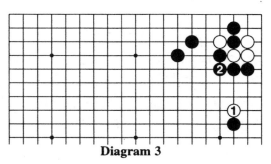

Diagram 3

86

Sabaki [Fancy Footwork]

PROBLEM NUMBER 41

WHITE TO PLAY

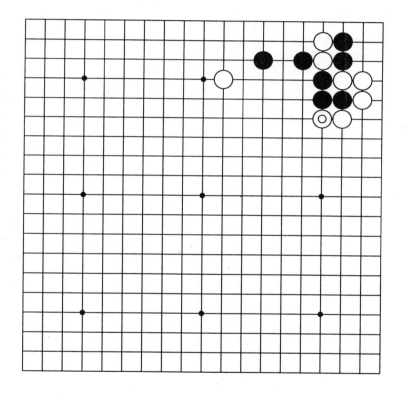

This shape often can be seen in actual games, but what is white's best way of playing?

An approach that is too complacent is no good. Notice also that white has pressed upward with the marked stone.

(15% respondent success rate)

Solution

Sacrifice Stones to Wrap Up the Opponent

Solution Diagram The proper form of play and good shape of stones regularly undergo variation according to the surroundings and circumstances in which the stones find themselves. Thus, in this problem if one thinks in too stereotypical or banal terms, one will not be able to come up with the correct answer.

After turning at white 1, capturing a stone with 3 & 5 follows a course of events that is often seen, but the question is what to do when black plays atari at 6. The counter-atari of white 7 here is a move that demands imaginative ability beyond the average. After black captures two stones with 8...

Diagram 1 (A complete wrap-up) With 9 & 11, white wraps black's stones up with a feeling of satisfaction, and then connecting at 13 finishes off this sequence that has been played in precisely the correct move order. After this, forcing moves (kikashi) at white **a** and **b** remain, while white's outward influence leaves nothing to be desired.

Diagram 2 (Not the standard shape) When black plays atari at 6, capturing the two black stones in the corner with white 7 is a standard technique, but only when the marked white stone has not been played. In this situation, after black plays at 10 the thick and thin positions have been reversed.

Diagram 3 (Playing without a plan) Extending to white 1 is useless, since it lets black capture at 2. Even though white can squeeze with the move at **a**, the difference between this and the **Solution Diagram** is as great as night and day.

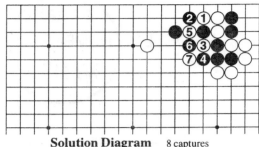

Solution Diagram   8 captures

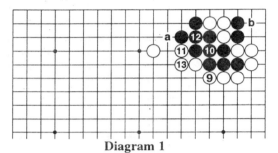

Diagram 1

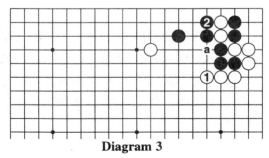

Diagram 2   8 captures

Diagram 3

88

Sabaki [Fancy Footwork]

PROBLEM NUMBER 42

BLACK TO PLAY

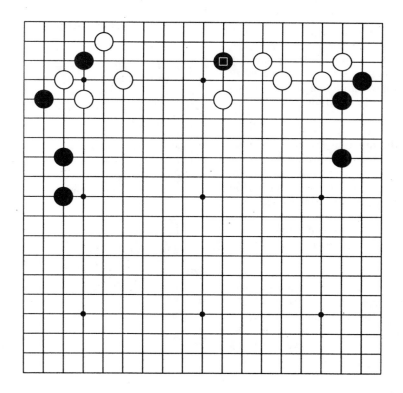

The focus is on how black can manage the situation (sabaki) that the marked stone is in.

No matter what, it can not easily be captured, but if matters are artfully handled (sabaki), nothing could be better. Start by using defects (aji) in the upper left corner.

(17% respondent success rate)

Solution

Poking at the Vital Point

Solution Diagram Starting maneuvers at the vital point of black 1 is the best way to handle the situation [sabaki]. Black seeks to get every ounce of value [aji] from the stone that has been captured in the corner.

If white butts against black's stone with 2, black extends upward with 3, and when white plays 4 & 6, black fearlessly hanes in return at 7. Then, if white goes to capture two black stones with 8 & 10, black winds up playing a nicely satisfying atari at 13.

Diagram 1 (A full measure of profit) If white uses the move at 8 in the previous diagram to take one stone with 1 & 3, black will push through at 4 and then play at 6 & 8 to take advantage of weaknesses [aji] in the corner. Even though black cedes outward influence to white in the moves through black 12, the profit gained in the corner is enough to allay any misgivings.

Diagram 2 (Thickness for white) A go proverb advises, "Play a knight's move in response to a capping move!" but if black plays at 1 here, the attachment of white 2 will insure that black's dodging maneuvers [sabaki] do not come off as well as black would like. Black has no trouble living with the moves following 3, but the thickness white builds while black is doing so is far and away superior.

Diagram 3 (The limitations of "rules of thumb") The two space extension of black 1 cannot be characterized as a bad move, but when white seals black in with 2 there is an oppressively claustrophobic feeling about the position. Undoubtedly, black will succeed only in living here.

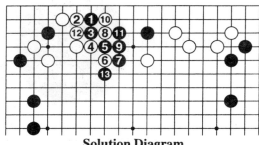

Solution Diagram

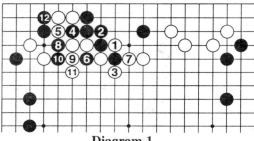

Diagram 1

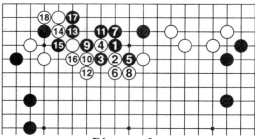

Diagram 2

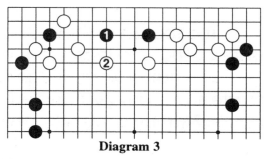

Diagram 3

Sabaki [Fancy Footwork]

PROBLEM NUMBER 43

BLACK TO PLAY

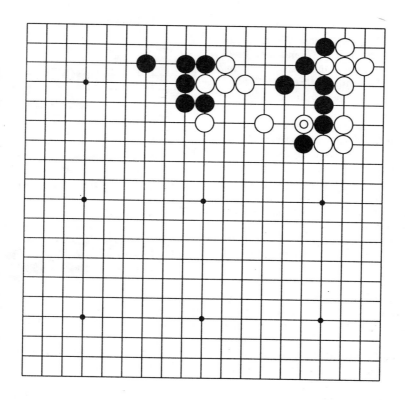

Here white has just cut with the marked stone. Black seems to be in a painfully difficult position. How can this group get through the crisis (shinogi)?

One precondition to factor in is that there are no large ko threats on the board elsewhere.

(20% respondent success rate)

Solution

Escape with Ease

Solution Diagram Accepting the capture at black 1 & 3 as the normal continuation, getting sealed in with white 2 & 4 would seem to make the whole position unplayable, but the anomalies in the shape here mean that the attachment of black 5 is a good move that insures the survival [shinogi] of black's stones. White has no choice but to answer at 6, and then black plays atari right back against white with 7 & 9, and with the moves through 17, black bursts out into the open with a comfortable position.

Diagram 1 (White at a loss) When black attaches at 5, the crux of the matter is that white cannot cut this stone off with a move at 6. With the stones positioned as they are, black cuts with 7 & 9 and white is at a loss for an answer. If white now takes the ko, black plays at **a** and white not only loses the two stones here, but the whole white group to the left winds up in a painfully difficult position.

Diagram 2 (A questionable order of moves) If black starts by playing 1 in this sequence, and then, if white answers at **a**, the variation reverts to the move order of the **Solution Diagram**. However, white will resist following orders, and play 2 & 4. This leads to the fencing in move of 8, which puts black in a quandary. A difference in the order of moves often results in correct playing form turning into no form at all.

Diagram 3 (White is thin) Such being the case, white might try extending to 2, but black 3 exposes the thinness of white's position. A comparison with the previous diagram points up the difference.

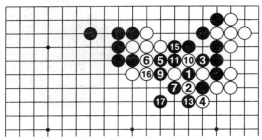

Solution Diagram 8 takes ko; 12, 14: connects

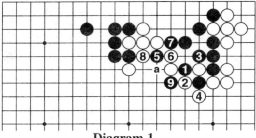

Diagram 1

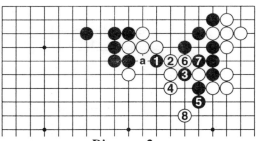

Diagram 2

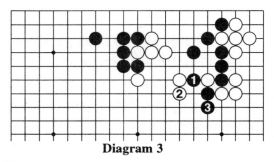

Diagram 3

92

Sabaki [Fancy Footwork]

PROBLEM NUMBER 44

BLACK TO PLAY

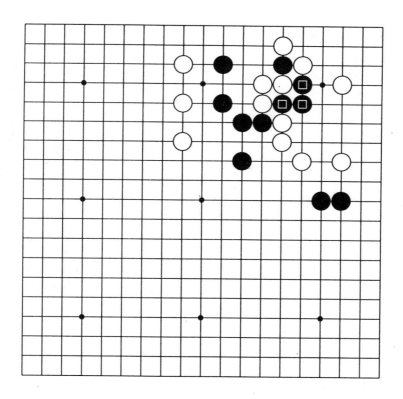

.It looks as though the three marked black stones within white's territory are completely dead. However, white's shape is not perfect either. If one plays the proper sequence of moves to take advantage of the opponent's defects, a good result may be obtained.

(15% respondent success rate)

Solution

Make Life Within the Opponent's Territory

Solution Diagram Cutting into white's position with the move at 1 is black's only hope for using the three stones that white has captured. If black plays atari at 2 here, white connects at 1 and black loses all the possibilities that had existed in this area.

In response, drawing back to white 2 is par for the situation, so the moves from black 3 through 8 are inevitable. Then black gets great satisfaction in plastering white in with 9 & 13 before making life with 17.

Diagram 1 (Terrible for white) If white captures one stone with 2 when black cuts at 1, then black plays atari at 3 and connects at 5. White must now face black's threat of finding play within white's own corner. If white hangs tough and draws back to 6, the hanging connection of black 7 is a good move. White is hampered by the fact that connecting underneath at 10 cannot be omitted. The result to black 15 is the worst possible outcome for white.

Diagram 2 (Ko) Also, after playing 1 & 3, black must not be in too much of a hurry to play at 5 in order to seek life. When white descends to 6, black is unable to live unconditionally.

Diagram 3 (No move this way) It is bad for black to first run out with 1. This is a mistake in the order of moves and it is bad. After black 3 & 5, white connects at 6, giving white the option [aji] of playing at **a**, meaning that white has moves to play and black does not.

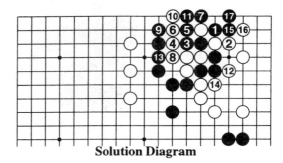

Solution Diagram

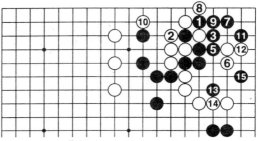

Diagram 1   4 connects

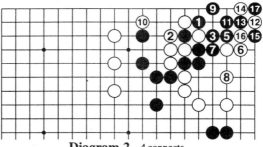

Diagram 2   4 connects

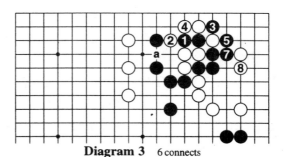

Diagram 3   6 connects

94

Sabaki [Fancy Footwork]

PROBLEM NUMBER 45

BLACK TO PLAY

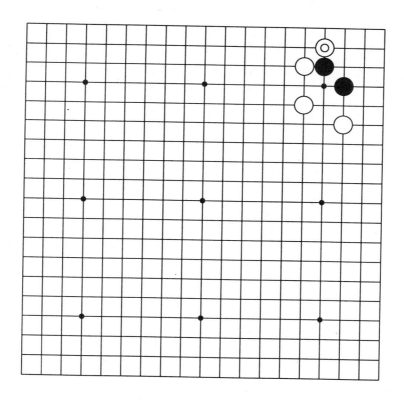

White has just played the hane with the marked stone. It is a simple matter to just make life in a mediocre manner, but one must think of a way to squeeze even one extra ounce of profit from the situation.

Sometimes a crude move is effective.

(12% respondent success rate)

Solution

Playing a Crude Move is Effective

Solution Diagram Black plays the diagonal attachment at 1. Since this is a crude move, it goes a bit against the grain to play in this way, but after exchanging this move for white 2, black will cut at 3, and the "crude move" here works better than one might think as a "skillful finesse" [tesuji]. It may be expected that white will play conventionally and connect at 4, and then black can take a stone with 5, living while preserving opportunities [aji] for later. If white extends to **a** with 4, black is left with the opportunity [aji] to cut at **b**.

Diagram 1 (Reading with rose colored glasses) Black might play the trite blocking move at 1, and if white is considerate enough to play 2 & 4, black can be satisfied at that. Taking a stone with 5 & 7 allows black to live in sente. However, white will not play this way.

Diagram 2 (Unsatisfactory) When black blocks at 1, the simple connection of white 2 is the most disagreeable move that black could be confronted with. Black then attaches with 3, desperately seeking a way to make life for the group, but after white plays at 6, black must play one more move in the corner to prevent an attachment at **a** by white.

Diagram 3 (Black is captured) Attaching with black 1 and cutting at 3 is not possible. White plays 4 & 6, and with the moves through 12, black's group has been captured en masse.

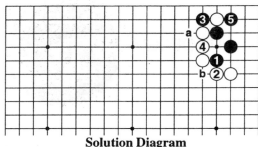

Solution Diagram

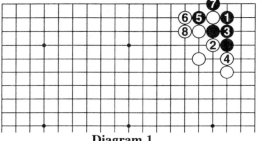

Diagram 1

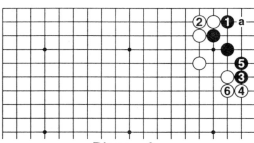

Diagram 2

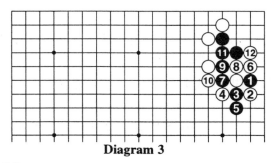

Diagram 3

96

Sabaki [Fancy Footwork]

PROBLEM NUMBER 46

WHITE TO PLAY

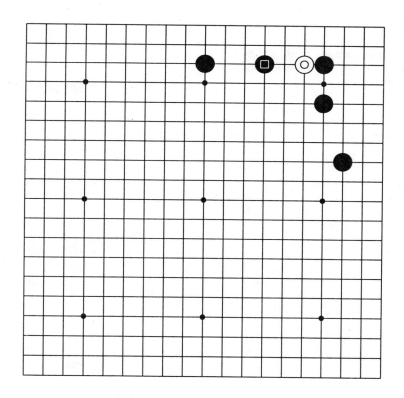

Black has come pressing in with the marked stone. It may appear that all the life in white's marked stone has slipped away, but the lone white fighting force still has guerrilla tactics (sabaki) at its command.

(22% respondent success rate)

Solution

Play with a Light and Easy Touch

Solution Diagram· Always viewing stones as light and easily expendable is the standard one must use in handling difficult situations flexibly and effectively [sabaki]. In this problem as well, moving out directly would be too heavy, and only betray one's ignorance of that principle. In this diagram, attaching at white 1 is correct, which in the situation shown is just common sense.

After connecting at 2, black cuts at 4. With the move at 5, white follows the go proverb that states: "Capture the cutting stone." Taking the corner is a great success for white.

Diagram 1 (A variation) If black uses 2 in the previous diagram to descend at 2 here, then white will naturally wedge into black's position with 3. Next, no matter which side that black makes at cut on following this, white will connect on the opposite side and get a good result. For example, if black plays at 4 as in this diagram, white plays 5 through 9, handling the situation [sabaki] in a way that is not inferior to the last diagram.

Diagram 2 (Squirming) Directly moving out with a weak, solitary stone is to be avoided at all cost. Rather than being a model of "fancy footwork" [sabaki], the moves at 1 & 3 show white "squirming" in a difficult situation. And there is no guarantee that these stones will not end up being captured en masse.

Diagram 3 (Simply running away) Playing a hane into black's position is also heavy. Even though white 7 & 9 are good form, with the moves through 15, white only succeeds in getting to run away.

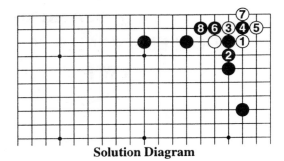

Solution Diagram

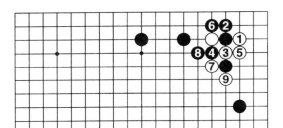

Diagram 1

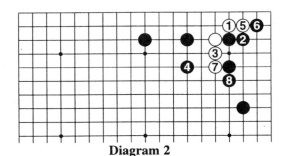

Diagram 2

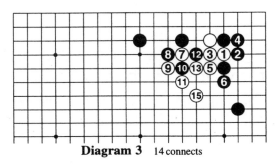

Diagram 3 14 connects

98

Sabaki [Fancy Footwork]

PROBLEM NUMBER 47

BLACK TO PLAY

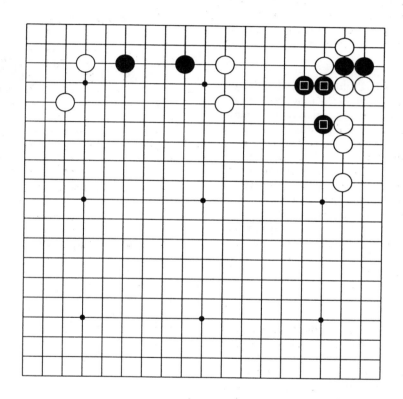

This problem does not revolve around saving the two black stones in the corner. The focal point is the skillful disposition of the three marked black stones in the center.

Naturally, here one must consider the possibilities that are afforded by the sacrifice stones in the corner.

(34% respondent success rate)

Solution

Two Good points of Equal Value [Miai]

Solution Diagram It is correct to play the knight's move of black 1 here, which makes the cut at **a** and connecting underneath at 5 good moves that are of equal value [miai]. If white defends against the cut at **a** with 2 & 4, black gets a sufficient result by connecting underneath at 5.

Diagram 1 (Problems [aji] linger) By simply attaching with the move at 1, black has a cunning and concealed aim. If white blocks at **a**, black will play at **b**, or else, if white extends at **b**, black will play the two-pronged attacking move at 2. In either of these cases, black would garner a better result than in the **Solution Diagram**. However, white will not hane at **a**, but instead use a dodging strategy and play the move at 2. Even if black cuts at 3, and plays the sequence through 9, white is left with the moves at **a** & **b**, etc., and this cannot be considered the best way for black to handle the situation [sabaki].

Diagram 2 (No good continuation) The attachment of white 1 looks like a skillful finesse [tesuji], but white makes a hard-nosed answer with the move at 2, and black still has to deal with the cut at **a**. There is no follow-up move for black in the situation here.

Diagram 3 (The worst thing to do) With the moves at 1 & 3, black tries to live in the corner, but after extending to 4, white has gotten the opportunity to aim at playing white **a**, black **b**, and white **c**.

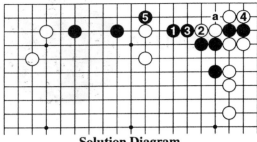

Solution Diagram

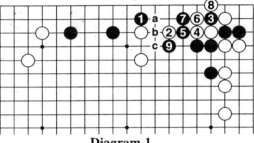

Diagram 1

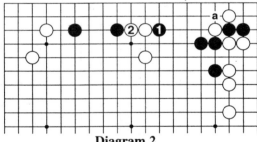

Diagram 2

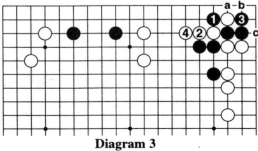

Diagram 3

Sabaki [Fancy Footwork]

PROBLEM NUMBER 48

BLACK TO PLAY

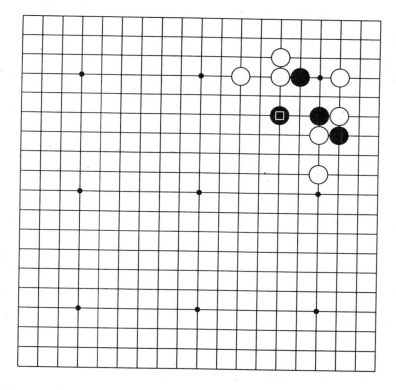

This is a standard model of skillful maneuvering (sabaki) that also often appears in real games.

Using the marked black stone in the most effective way possible is what is called for. A precondition for this type of problem is that the ladder is in black's favor.

(8% respondent success rate)

Solution

Atari Twice, then Make a Connection

Solution Diagram After fixing the shape with the moves at 1 & 3, playing atari on both sides, black connects at 5. With the shape of the stones in this sort of position, this is a prototypical technique for using one's stones effectively [sabaki]. If white defends against the ladder by playing at 6, black pushes through at 7, and by finishing up with the move at 9, black makes a comfortable life while laying waste to white's corner in fine style. As an aside it should be noted that the move order of black 1 & 3, and that of black 5 & 7 may be reversed with the same result.

Diagram 1 (Black is overconcentrated) If black plays atari first with 1 and then connects at 3, white will get the chance to cross underneath with 4, and then play 6 & 8. The result here is nothing less than that black needlessly makes heavy shape for the stones. Can the reader see that the bad shape that black's marked stone makes is a source of concern?

Diagram 2 (Vital point) Black cannot expect to make good shape by playing the atari of 1 and followed by the connection of 3. Even though black answers white 4 by making the atari at 5 and then 7, when white connects at 8, the marked white stone turns out to be an attachment at the vital point. This cannot be considered a fruitful result [sabaki] for black.

Diagram 3 (Crude move) If black could deal with matters well [sabaki] with the atari at 1 & 3, then this would not be much of a problem. But the result here is that white is deliberately given more solid shape.

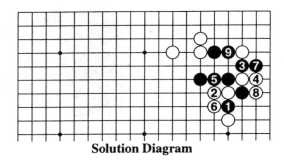

Solution Diagram

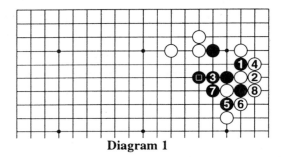

Diagram 1

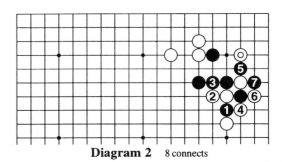

Diagram 2   8 connects

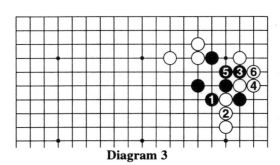

Diagram 3

102

Sabaki [Fancy Footwork]

PROBLEM NUMBER 49

BLACK TO PLAY

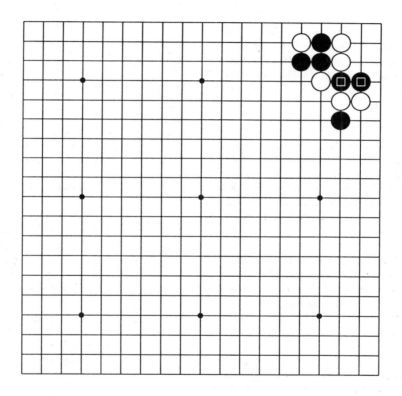

It is typical of amateurs to attempt to save stones that seem in danger of being captured. It is typical of professionals to discard such stones.

In this problem, trying to save the two marked black stones is no good. Find the best way to discard them.

(10% respondent success rate)

Solution

Sacrifice the Stones to Make a Squeeze Play

Solution Diagram Whether one is to save the two black stones on the right side or sacrifice them, if black does not start by cutting at 1, there is nothing to talk about. Then, using the impetus gained by forcing white to play at 2, black extends to 3, a move that displays the sensitivity of a professional. When white captures at 4, black boxes white in with the move at 5. The continuation through 11 allows black to build impressive thickness.

Diagram 1 (Black gets even greater thickness) When black plays 1 & 3, the atari of white 4 is a bad move. When black gets to fence white in with the moves at 5 & 7, the thickness thereby created is all the more greater than that in the **Solution Diagram**.

Diagram 2 (Inadequate fence) Black 5 here is a somewhat unorthodox fencing-in move, but white is inadequately sealed in. White plays 6 and cuts at 8, and can also consider playing white 6 at **a**, and when black replies at **b**, push out at white **c**.

Diagram 3 (The worst thing to do) If black plays 1 & 3, the two white stones can be captured, but since the three black stones on the upper side are captured, black has accomplished nothing.

The respondent success rate for this problem was only 10%. This fact exposes the weakness in amateurs' perception: when faced with problems that demand sacrificing stones, they are often unsuccessful.

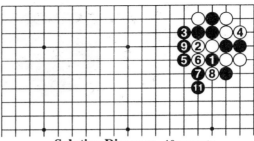

Solution Diagram   10 connects

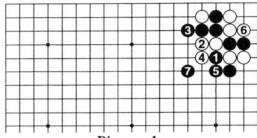

Diagram 1

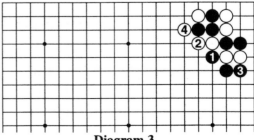

Diagram 2

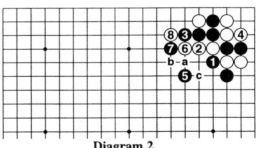

Diagram 3

104

PROBLEM

Sabaki [Fancy Footwork]

NUMBER 50

WHITE TO PLAY

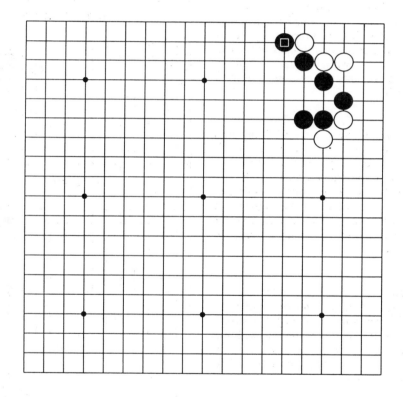

Black has just played the two-step hane of the marked stone. Answering carelessly will set oneself up to be tricked. Where should white play the next move?

(42% respondent success rate)

Solution

The Correct Line of Play Demands a Hane

Solution Diagram Black's aim in this situation is to capture the two white stones in the corner and attack white's stones on the right side. Therefore, by playing the hane at 1, white avoids falling into that trap. If black cuts at 2, white pulls back at 3, then cuts at 5. After this, the preparatory moves of white 1 & 3 mean that if black plays at **a**, white **b**, black **c**, white **d**, black **e**, white's answer at **f** prevents this continuation from being feasible.

Diagram 1 (Next best) Wedging into black's position with 1 will also allow white to make adequate shape, more or less. However, viewing the result after black 8, one perceives that shape of white's position in the corner is incomplete, and at some point in the future it may become necessary for white to add the moves white **a**, black **b**, and white **c**.

Diagram 2 (White at a disadvantage) If white starts off by playing the atari at 1, black will cut at 4 and can then put up strong resistance using refined technique with the moves at 6 & 8. Perhaps the reader can see that the fight after black plays at 16 will be more favorable for black.

Diagram 3 (Insufficient for black) The connection of white 1 falls right in line with black's wishes. When black plays 2, and then captures the two white stones in the corner with the moves through 8, white is left with weak stones on both the upper side and the right side.

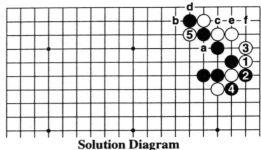

Solution Diagram

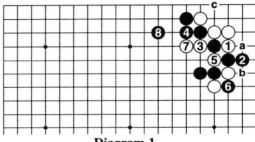

Diagram 1

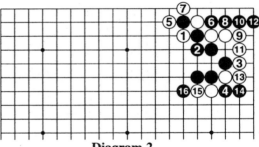

Diagram 2

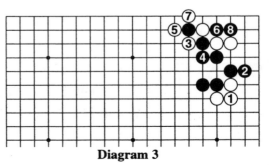

Diagram 3

106

PROBLEM

Sabaki [Fancy Footwork]

NUMBER 51

WHITE TO PLAY

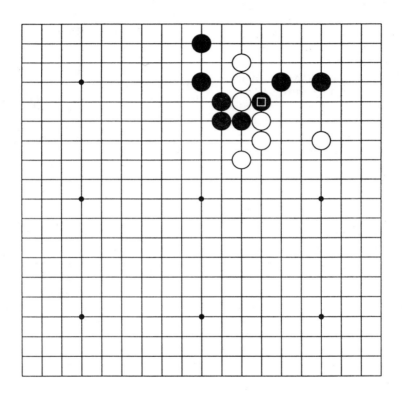

After being cut by the marked black stone, it is impossible for white's three stones either to escape or to live independently.

However, there are various dodging techniques (sabaki) to use. What is the best way to play?

(27% respondent success rate)

107

Solution

Playing Simply and Directly is Correct

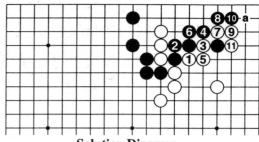

Solution Diagram

Solution Diagram There are situations where the best thing to do is to actually just play the simple, blatant move that would occur to anyone. In such a way, the atari of white 1, and the wedge into black's position with 3, is the best variation to adopt in order to solve this problem. If black responds by defending from below with 4, white connects at 5. The variation will then proceed inevitably with the moves through 11. Black has merely managed to secure the profit on the upper side in sente, but one must not fail to see that white can in the endgame play the big move at **a** in sente.

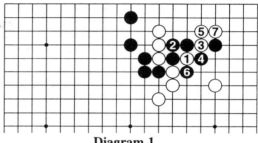

Diagram 1

Diagram 1 (Variation) Suppose that when white plays the moves at 1 & 3 to wedge into black's position, black cuts at 4; white draws away at 5, then turns at 7, and everything is right in the world for white. No matter how tough black tries to make things, a disadvantage for white here is difficult to imagine.

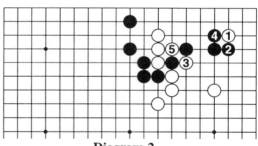

Diagram 2

Diagram 2 (The corner is big) It is also possible for white to start maneuvers in this area by simply invading at the 3-3 point in the corner. Black is induced to block at 2, and then the rhythm of the play of the stones dictate that white atari at 3. However, black will be pleased to disregard this to play at 4, and though white manages to rescue the three white stones, the loss of the corner looms large.

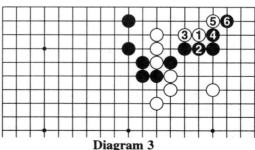

Diagram 3

Diagram 3 (Not alive) White might try to poke at 1 but when black connects at 2, there is no follow-up move. If white plays at 3 & 5, black 6 leaves the white group without eyes.

Sabaki [Fancy Footwork]

PROBLEM NUMBER 52

WHITE TO PLAY

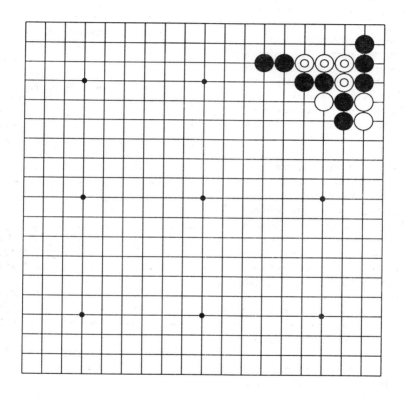

    If the ladder was favorable, white would have an easy time of it, but in this situation the ladder is assumed to be good for black. In that case, it is unreasonable to try to save the four marked white stones. The question is how to discard them.

(24% respondent success rate)

Solution

First Make a Diagonal Move, Then Squeeze

Solution Diagram The best way to wrap black up and squeeze is to play the diagonal move at white 1, and follow up as shown. Black has no choice but to play at 2, but white wraps black up and squeezes with 3 & 5, and after black 8 play comes to a lull. Considering the matter from white's perspective, this is the best result that can be expected in this situation. There is no more effective continuation [sabaki] that can be made here. If, while playing this variation, black plays 2 at 4, white plays at 2, black **a**, white 5: black is annihilated.

Diagram 1 (Next best) One may also consider playing the fencing-in move of white 1. After the moves from black 2 through 8, an unforked continuation, white plays 9 & 11, now wrapping black up in this way. At first glance, the variation through white 17 seems to be a wonderfully successful resolution, but do not fail to notice that, in comparison with the **Solution Diagram**, white has lost the two stones on the right side, and also, there is a cutting point at **a** for white to deal with. One must conclude that this is a second-best strategy.

Diagram 2 (Insufficient for white) White plays atari at 1, then blocks at 3. When white plays at 5, black captures with 6. White 7 will be followed by black 8. This leaves another cutting point at **a**. This cutting point that has been left means that the fencing-in operation has been less than successful.

Diagram 3 (Without a plan) It is not good enough to play the bland atari of 1 & 3 since these moves pass up opportunities. This shows the bankruptcy of own's strategy.

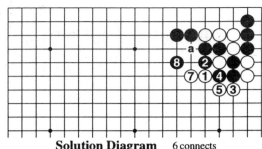

Solution Diagram   6 connects

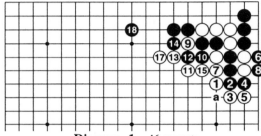

Diagram 1   16 connects

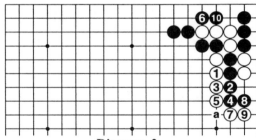

Diagram 2

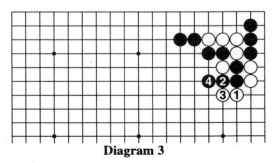

Diagram 3

PROBLEM NUMBER 53

Sabaki [Fancy Footwork]

WHITE TO PLAY

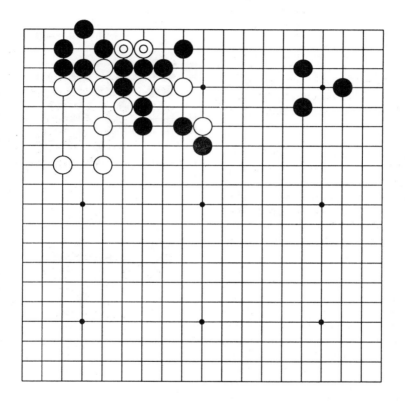

White's sundry stones encircled by black are in an agonizingly difficult position. But there is a skillful finesse (tesuji) that can be used here to almost magically allow white to escape this torture.

The dead marked white stones are used effectively.

(17% respondent success rate)

Solution

A Decisive Cut Settles Matters

Solution Diagram The decisive cut of white 1 is an exquisitely skillful finesse [tesuji] that probes black's response. This time it is black that has the tables turned and is hard pressed to deal with the situation [sabaki].

If black plays 2 & 4, the moves of 5 & 7 are ones that white has had in reserve from the start. With the sequence through 13, white deftly handles the situation [sabaki], making ideal shape. At white 5...

Diagram 1 (Unreasonable for white) The extension of white 1 is a mistake in the proper order of moves. After black connects at 2, even if white plays at 3 & 5, black fixes the shape to white's detriment with 6 and the following, and there is no saving measure in sight for white.

Diagram 2 (Ko) Drawing back to white 1 here sometimes makes good form, but black extends to 2, and things will not go well for white. If white now attacks with 3 and the moves that follow, white precipitates a ko fight, but after 12, white has no suitable ko material with which to contest it. If white uses 3 to cut at **a**, black answers with **b**, white **c**, and then black fences white in with a move at **d**.

Diagram 3 (Black is well off) Fixing the shape first with white 1 & 3, and then cutting at 5 is a mistake in the order of moves. When black responds with 6 & 8, the difference compared to the **Solution Diagram** is obvious.

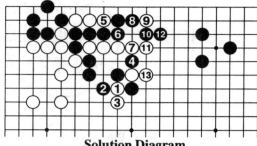

Solution Diagram

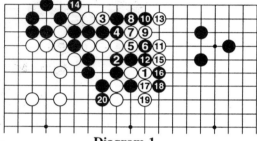

Diagram 1

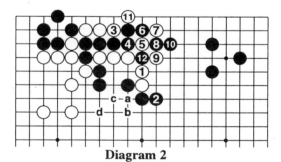

Diagram 2

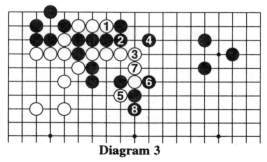

Diagram 3

112

Sabaki [Fancy Footwork]

PROBLEM NUMBER 54

BLACK TO PLAY

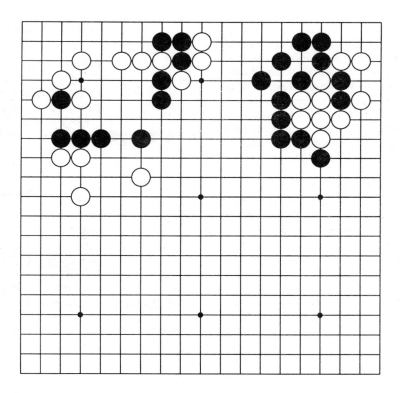

Simply rescuing the three black stones on the upper side is insufficient. One must at the same time secure the safety of the black stones on the left.

The first move in the correct sequence is easy to find, but the move order afterward is important.

(12% respondent success rate)

Solution

Indomitable Resistance

Solution Diagram First off: if black wants to save the three stones on the upper side, the only move to play is the cut at 1. When white extends at 2, black applies continuing pressure by playing at 3, and then extending to 5 is the correct move order. At first sight, this might seem to be a slack way of playing, but the real point of this problem is that when white replies at 6, black plays the hane at 7, a skillful finesse [tesuji] that has been black's principal aim from the very start, and which restricts white's options severely. The moves from white 8 through black 13 result in a position in which black has dealt with matters [sabaki] and has no problems whatsoever.

Diagram 1 (Black suffers a loss) Following black 1 & 3, playing atari at 5 might seem to be the most severe move possible, but when white captures at 6, black has no move to follow up with. Black's three captured stones on the upper side end up as an out and out loss for black.

Diagram 2 (Weak kneed) If one has gone so far as to play the correct move order up to black 5, in response to white 6, black must not give ground by replying at 7. Even though black's group on the left is safe, white captures black's three stones on the upper side. Black will be able to wrap white up and squeeze, starting with the move at **a**, but this is unsatisfactory.

Diagram 3 (Black in distress) After the exchange of black 1 for white 2, playing the attachment immediately at 3 is unreasonable. White cuts at 8, and the fact that white still has the option of capturing the three stones at **a** leaves black in distress.

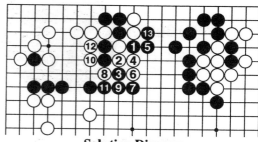

Solution Diagram

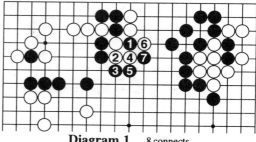

Diagram 1   8 connects

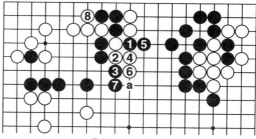

Diagram 2

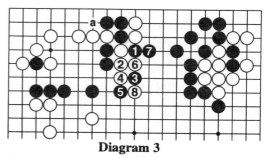

Diagram 3

114

PROBLEM **Reading** NUMBER 55
BLACK TO PLAY

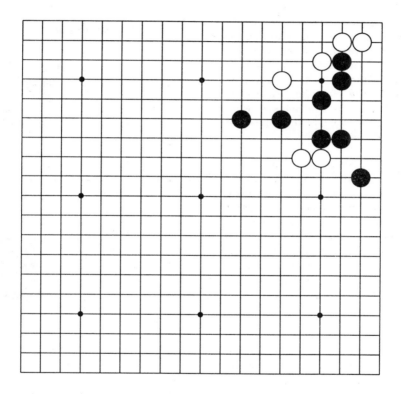

How can the white group in the upper right be attacked? Allowing such a thin group of stones to live easily
would be intolerable.

The essential thing is to find the first move, but parry-
ing white's responses also requires a bit of ingenuity.

(13% respondent success rate)

115

Solution

Making a Poke is the Strongest Move

Solution Diagram The way for black to initiate the strongest attack possible is to start with the poke at 1 here. In response, it is best for white to play downward with 2. It is then natural for black to continue the attack with the moves from 3 through 9, but white throws in the cut at 10, an extremely skillful move that leaves options for white later. The moves through 21 comprise an inevitable line of play, and it seems like all of white's stones have been taken, while it is only the black side which has profited. However, after this...

Diagram 1 (White can live) Squeezing at white 1 & 3, and then descending to 5 are moves that remain at white's disposal because of the cut of the marked white stone that was thrown in previously. The upshot is that making life in the corner with a move at **a**, or connecting underneath at **b** are equivalent options [miai] for white. In regards to the connection underneath with white **b**, even if black exchanges **c** for white **d**, it has no bearing on the status of the connection.

Diagram 2 (White is completely destroyed) If, in reply to black 1, white connects at 2, a critical situation develops. Black seals white in with the moves from 3 through 7, and even though white can again make a squeeze play starting with 8, after black 13, white is completely destroyed.

Diagram 3 (White lives) Black 1 does not attack deeply enough and makes things easy for white. White plays at 2, and even if black plays at 3 & 5, white's group is alive just as it is.

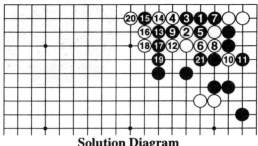

Solution Diagram

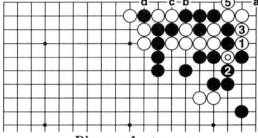

Diagram 1   4 connects

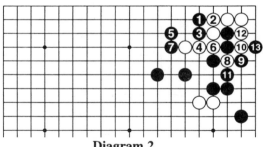

Diagram 2

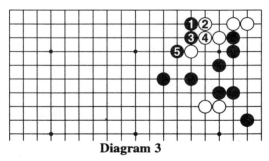

Diagram 3

116

PROBLEM **NUMBER 56**

WHITE TO PLAY

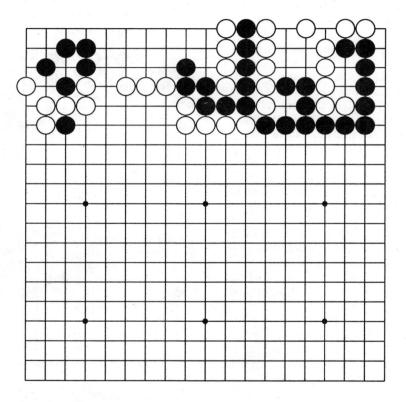

Can black be captured or can white? The best method to solve this circumscribed question is what is asked of the reader.

There are three liberties for both the black and white stones in the middle of the upper side. But white goes first.

(18% respondent success rate)

Solution

White Wins the Race to Capture [Semeai]

Solution Diagram Attack and defense of the stones on the upper side spills over into the upper left corner, and in the end, white wins the race to capture [semeai], effectively ending the game.

The first step is for white to start off by attaching at 1, and with the uncompromising play to 7, white fills in black's liberties. Then, when black plays at 8, white 9 is a skillful finesse [tesuji] that is a critically important component in this problem. Black cannot win the race to capture in the middle of the upper side, and so endeavors to connect forces with the move at 10, but white skillfully lives with 11 through 15, and with the moves up to 19, white wins the race to capture easily.

Diagram 1 (A double snap-back) If white prematurely blocks at 1 instead of playing 9 in the previous diagram, the race to capture will end with white's failure. Black 2 & 4 set up snap-backs on both sides, and white is lost.

Diagram 2 (Strong play, but...) There is some validity in trying to play the jump to white 1. After black 2, the moves through white 7 deprive the black group of eyes. However, black fixes the shape with 8 & 10, and then...

Diagram 3 (Black wins the ko) If black plays at 12 & 14 to try to connect underneath, with the moves through 21, a ko is unavoidable. However, at this point black 22 is a perfect ko threat that has to be answered, and so black ends up winning the ko fight.

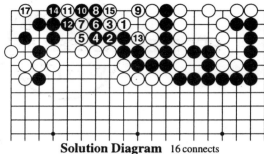

Solution Diagram 16 connects

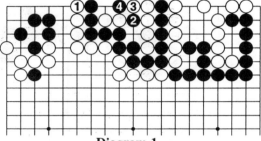

Diagram 1

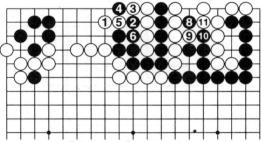

Diagram 2 7: throw-in at 3

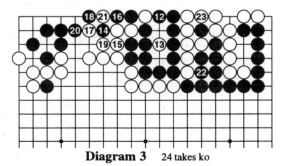

Diagram 3 24 takes ko

118

PROBLEM **Reading NUMBER 57 WHITE** TO PLAY

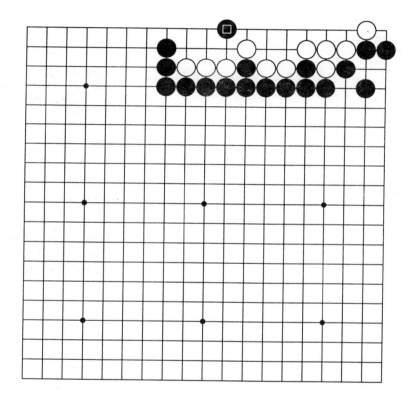

Black has come sliding in with the marked stone. If white just blithely responds, it will be impossible to make two eyes.

If both sides play the most accurate sequence of moves, how can white make life?

(18% respondent success rate)

Solution

Make Life for Half of the Group

Solution Diagram It is unreasonable for white to try to make life for all of the stones here. Regardless, the attachment of white 1 to start off represents the only technique available to make eyes. Then, when black plays at 2, blocking at white 3 is the proper continuation. If black cuts at 4, playing 5 through 9 enables white to just barely manage to insure life for the left half of the group.

Diagram 1 (Black incurs a loss) When white makes the attachment at 1, cutting at with the move at black 2 cannot be considered the best reply. The connection of white 3 is a calm and collected move, and there is no move at black's disposal to take away the eyes of white stones to the right. In the end, with the moves through 7, white makes life for the major portion of the group, and this sequence exemplifies failure on black's part.

Diagram 2 (The white group dies) Simply playing the block at 1 will not enable white to make eyes for this group as a whole. Black cuts with the move at 2 and descends to 4, and with that the white group is finished off.

Diagram 3 (Simplistic) Connecting with the move at white 1 is answered by black's drawing back with the move at 2, leaving white's group dead. In addition, if white plays 1 at **a**, black **b**, white **c**, and black **d** results in death for the white group in this way as well.

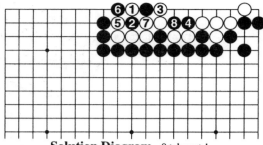

Solution Diagram   9 takes at 1

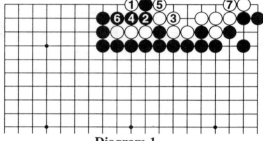

Diagram 1

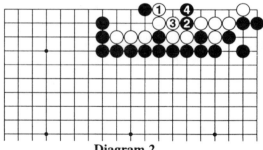

Diagram 2

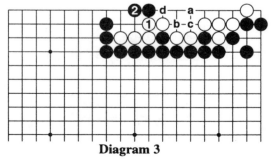

Diagram 3

PROBLEM NUMBER 58 — Reading — WHITE TO PLAY

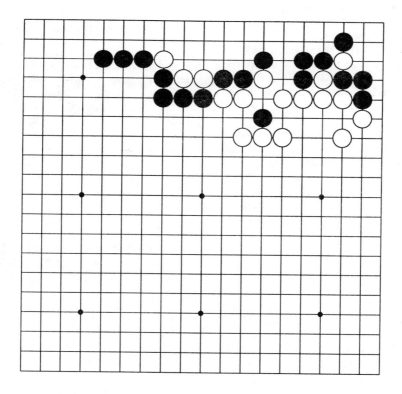

Black has such thin shape on the upper side that it seems that there must surely be an effective move to use against it. Where white should start is one thing, but too facile thinking will beckon unexpected resistance.

Making a ko here would represent success.

(22% respondent success rate)

Solution

Use the Correct Order of Moves to Make Ko

Solution Diagram Cutting first at white 1 is an absolutely essential move, but when black plays at 2, the consecutive hane of white 3 is the key in this position, a skillful finesse [tesuji] which is the only move here. If black captures with the move at 4, white plays atari at 5, fixing the shape, which allows white to put up the most stubborn resistance with the move at 7. By getting to make this kind of shape, white can easily precipitate a ko fight.

Diagram 1 (A variation) When white plays atari at 1 & 3, black might push out with the move at 4, but then the atari on the other side at white 5 comes into play. When black captures at 6, white plays atari at 7, and once again there is a ko fight. If black plays the move at 6 as an extension to 7, then white plays at 6, opening up a big hole in black's position.

Diagram 2 (A pitfall in the position) One might think that simply playing atari at white 1 & 3 will also lead to ko, but this is a one-sided reading of the situation. When white plays the move at 5, black can turn the tables by playing atari at 6 & 8, a technique that exposes the failure of white's play. Black's marked stone turns out to be effectively placed.

Diagram 3 (No move for white this way) For white to play the cut at 1 and then continuing with the descending move at 3 would also result in failure. After black plays atari at 4, white has no follow-up move. If white plays the move at 5 at 6 instead, black answers by playing at 5 and the outcome is the same.

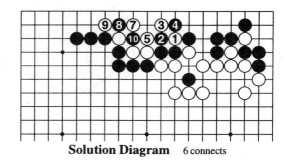

Solution Diagram   6 connects

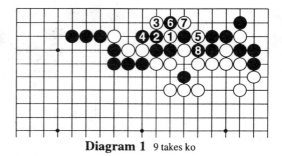

Diagram 1 9 takes ko

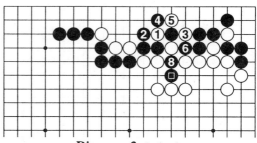

Diagram 2 7 takes ko

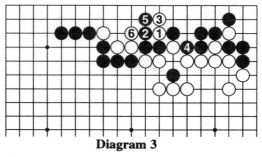

Diagram 3

122

PROBLEM NUMBER 59

Reading

BLACK TO PLAY

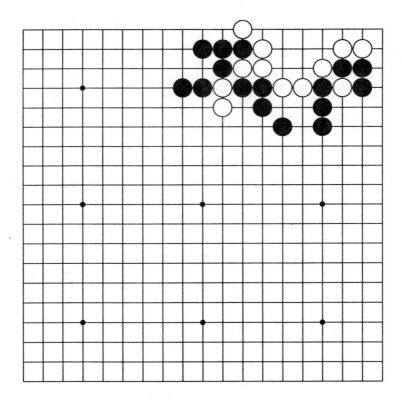

If black plays first in the corner, is there a move to capture white or not?

In the midst of the sequence that will ensue, determining the resources available to white requires meticulous reading.

(11% respondent success rate)

Solution

Even if Black Plays First, There is No Move Here

Solution Diagram The ironic twist to this problem is that no matter how black attacks this corner, white lives unconditionally. Naturally, to arrive at this conclusion, a considerable amount of accurate reading is required to back it up.

If black wants to try something here, the attachment at 1 is the place to start, and then extending to black 3 is the strongest continuation. However, at this point white has an exquisite move in the diagonal play at 4. In the end, it turns out that black has no move to create trouble here, and this is the correct solution.

Diagram 1 (White dies) In response to black 1 & 3, connecting at white 4 is no good. Black descends to 5, and no matter what white tries or how much resistance white mounts, the group here will die unconditionally.

Diagram 2 (Half of the group lives) If one is unable to analyze the situation thoroughly through to the exquisite move of white 4 in the **Solution Diagram**, then when black attaches at 1, one has no choice but to play the diagonal attachment of white 2. In this case, white ends up securing life on the smallest scale possible, incurring substantial damage.

Diagram 3 (A bankrupt policy) If black makes a placement with 1, white will live with the move at 2. The result is the same as in the **Solution Diagram**, but one would like to see the most pressure possible to bear on white's position; it is pointless not to cause white serious discomfort.

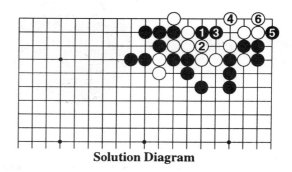

Solution Diagram

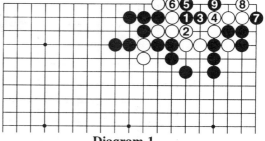

Diagram 1

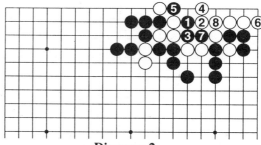

Diagram 2

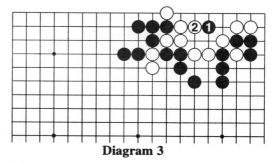

Diagram 3

(Reading NUMBER 60 WHITE) TO PLAY

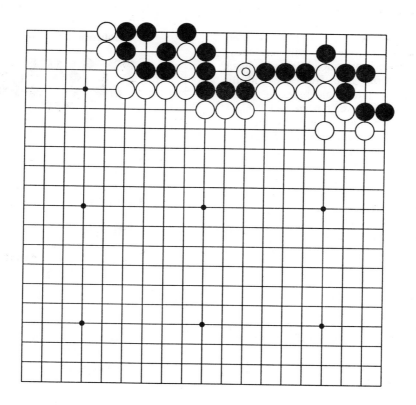

How can white use the marked stone to generate possibilities here? Naturally, black's shortage of liberties is to be aimed at, but the correct answer will be determined by finding the right move in the right shape.

(19% respondent success rate)

Solution

Make a One Move Approach Move Ko

Solution Diagram Starting operations with the hane of white 1 is a crucially important move. When black replies at 2, white fixes the shape with 3, and then the move of white 5 is played at the vital point. No matter how black answers this move, there will be problems to reckon with. The strongest resistance is provided by playing black 6 and connecting at 8. However, with the exchange of white 9 and black 10, a one move approach move ko is created. If black plays the move of 8 at 10, white captures at 9, and when black plays at 8, the white move at **a** makes the ko a direct one.

Diagram 1 (A variation) When white pokes at 5, if black forces at 6 and throws the stone in at 8, a complicated variation is produced. If white plays 9 at 10, black connects at 9 creating a situation where one side (black's group) has an eye and the other side (white's group) does not, meaning that white is simply dead. Therefore, white has no choice but to play at 9 & 11. After this...

Diagram 2 (Cyclical recapture) When black throws in the stone at 12, the move of white 13 will initiate a cyclical capture and recapture of two stones by each side, a shape that is considered to void the game. Of course, if black plays the move at 12 at 13, white plays at 12 and the situation reverts to the one in the **Solution Diagram** and a one move approach move ko.

Diagram 3 (Seki) White has one other technique that may be adopted in this situation. When white plays 1 & 3, if black avoids the ko fight, with the moves through 15, white turns the position into seki.

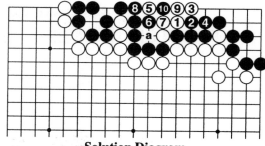

Solution Diagram

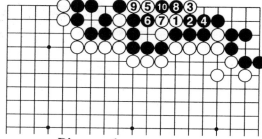

Diagram 1   11 takes two stones at 5

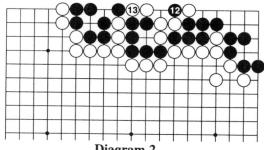

Diagram 2

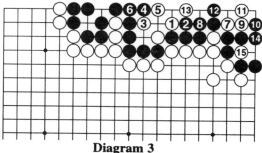

Diagram 3

PROBLEM

Reading
NUMBER 61
BLACK TO PLAY

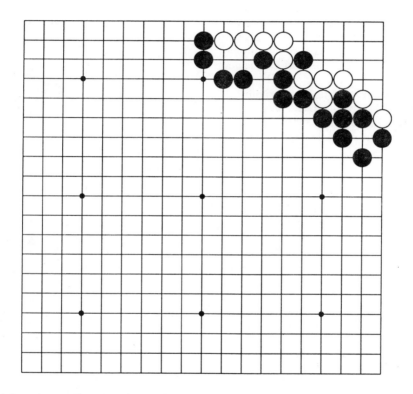

What kind of move can be used against white's corner? Just playing an ordinary endgame move here would be vacuous.

If one just discovers the first move which is the vital point, playing out the rest of the sequence is simple.

(26% respondent success rate)

Solution

The Vital Point is an Attachment

Solution Diagram The attachment of black is the vital point here. In response, pushing through with white 2 is the best move, but black plays atari at 3 and after 5, makes the hanging connection at 7, and no matter what happens, some kind of play will develop here. If white plays at 8 & 10 to deprive black of two eyes, it is very important to make the throw-in at black 11, and then, by pitching the stone in at 13, black starts a ko fight. Within this variation, if black plays 7 at 9, white **a**, and black 7 also results in ko, but if black simply plays 11 at 13, white connects at 11, and black has failed.

Diagram 1 (A two-step ko) When black attaches at 1, if white hanes at 2, playing atari at black 3, and then hane at 5 is good. After cutting at 6, white 8 & 10 are moves that put up stiff resistance, but the result is a two-step ko that is disadvantageous for white.

Diagram 2 (Bad form) The diagonal move of black 1 misses the vital point. White answers at 2 and there is nothing more that black can do. No matter what black tries after this, there is no move here to create any trouble.

Diagram 3 (Endgame moves) Cutting with the move at black 1 here is nothing more than a run-of-the-mill endgame play. When white replies by playing at 2, there is no trouble at all that white has to fear occurring.

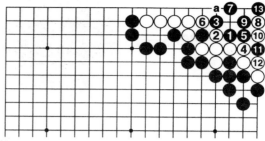

Solution Diagram

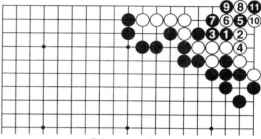

Diagram 1

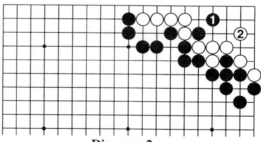

Diagram 2

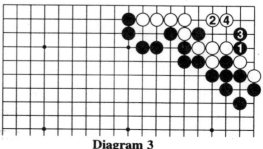

Diagram 3

128

PROBLEM **Reading** NUMBER 62
BLACK TO PLAY

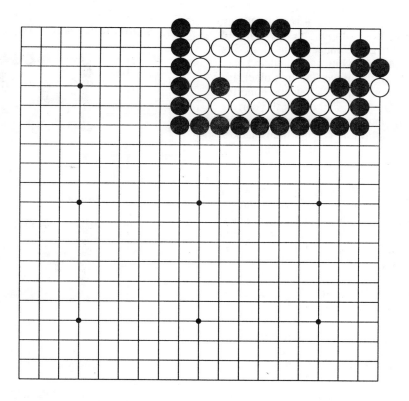

The boundary within which one must read is tightly confined, but this is quite a difficult problem.

In order to take away white's eye space, should one start from the inside or outside? White has good moves to resist with as well.

(11% respondent success rate)

Solution

Start a Ko Fight in the Corner

Solution Diagram Unless black plays at 1 within white's group to prevent white from making two eyes, there is nothing to be done. When white responds at 2, black plays at 3, but here white 4 is an exquisite play that makes it impossible for white to be killed outright. Connecting at black 5 is the best reply, but white hanes at 6 and play proceeds with the moves through black 13. A ko results, which black gets the opportunity to capture first, and this is the correct solution. If black uses the move at 9 to atari at 11, white plays at 12, and then black 9 ends up with a ko in which it is white's turn to take first.

Diagram 1 (Black is captured) When white plays the attachment of 4, trying to intercept and trap white by playing at black 5 is unreasonable. White pokes at 6 and cuts at 8, leaving black stymied due to a shortage of liberties.

Diagram 2 (White dies) If white pushes out at 4, black can connect underneath at 5. When white plays at 6, black answers at 7 and white's group is unconditionally dead. Other than this, if white plays the move at 4 as an attachment at 6, black plays at 4 and the result is the same. The fact is, white's attachment at **a** is the exquisite move in this situation.

Diagram 3 (White lives) It is bad for black to begin operations against the white group by playing from the outside with the move at 1. By adding a stone here, giving black a clump of three stones, black loses the option of crossing underneath with a move at **a**.

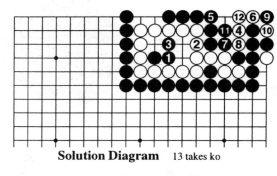

Solution Diagram   13 takes ko

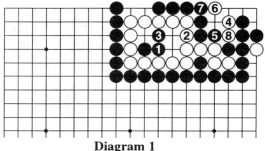

Diagram 1

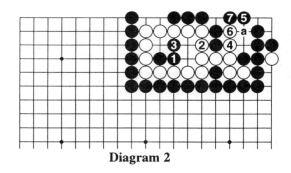

Diagram 2

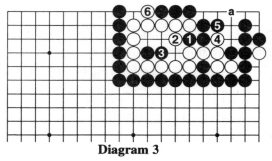

Diagram 3

130

PROBLEM  TO PLAY

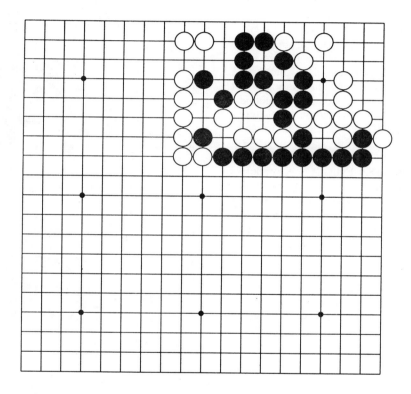

If white plays first, can black be captured or not? In the final analysis, attack and defense in the corner is the focal point.

Black can tenaciously resist, so it is necessary for white to read past that. If a ko results, white has failed.

(9% respondent success rate)

Solution

An Exquisitely Played Jump

Solution Diagram In order to prevent white from making a second eye, the throw-in at black 2 is the only move here. If white instead plays at **a**, black can play the forcing moves [kikashi] at **b** and **c** in sente, living easily.

In response, the moves from black 2 through 6 offer the strongest resistance. However, here white defends by playing the exquisite jump to 7, and this is the correct order of moves, resulting in the unconditional death of black's group. Please confirm for yourself that black has no move to play here.

Diagram 1 (Ko fight) If one overlooks the exquisite jump at white 7 in the **Solution Diagram**, one would probably end up playing the block at white 7 here, but when black plays at 8 & 10, the cut at white 11 makes the ko fight that develops after 15 inevitable.

Diagram 2 (Simple) If black plays atari at 2 and pushes out at 4, white has no need to deploy exquisite survival maneuvers. The moves to white 9 comprise a simple sequence that results in the unconditional death of the black group.

Diagram 3 (An attack sputters out) After black plays the atari at 2, the two-step hane of black 4 can cause confusion, but with the moves from 5 through 11, white plays in a calm and collected manner that is the best way to handle the situation. After this, black might try to turn the position into a race to capture [semeai] by making a placement now at **a**, but that will not go well for black.

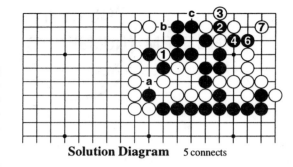

Solution Diagram   5 connects

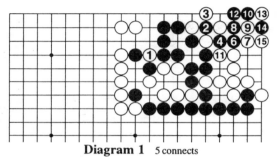

Diagram 1   5 connects

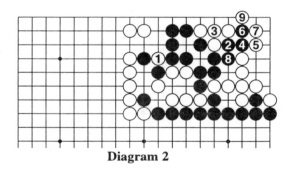

Diagram 2

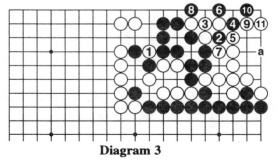

Diagram 3

132

PROBLEM — Reading NUMBER 64 — WHITE TO PLAY

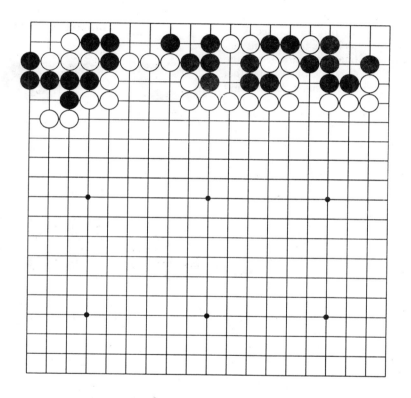

If one finds out where to play the first move, the following moves are easily found.

However, do not make the mistake of thinking that this is a run-of-the-mill life and death problem.

(17% respondent success rate)

Solution

The Best Result is for Both Sides to Live

Solution Diagram Jumping to white 1 is an absolutely essential move which aims at exploiting defects in the black groups to the left and right on the upper side. If one is unable to discover this move, one will not be able to solve this problem correctly. In response to this, black 2 is the best answer. At this point, the hane of white 3, and the attachment of 5 follow the line of play that is critically important in this situation, and then the moves from black 6 through 14 lead to both sides making life on the upper side. This is the correct solution to the problem. In this variation, if black plays the move at 6 at 7, white then plays at 10, black plays at 9, and with a white move at **a**, black's stones are captured.

Diagram 1 (A variation) When white plays the hane at 3, if black plays at 4, extending to white 5 is correct. After the exchange of black 6 and white 7, the variation returns to the move order of the **Solution Diagram**.

Diagram 2 (White incurs a loss) When black connects at 4, white 5 is a move that incurs a loss. Black blocks white off by playing at 6, and if white plays at 9, black can adopt the technique of sacrificing three stones with 10 & 12. The result that black obtains here is superior to the one shown in the **Solution Diagram**.

Diagram 3 (Black dies) Responding to white 1 with black 2, defending the stones on the right, is not possible. White 3 & 5 is a skillful finesse [tesuji], and with the moves through 9, black's stones in the corner end up dead.

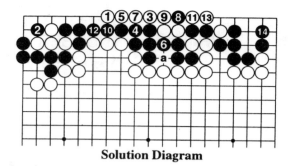

Solution Diagram

Diagram 1

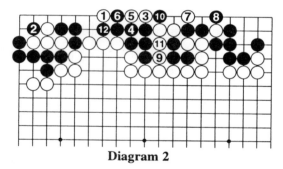

Diagram 2

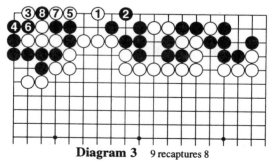

Diagram 3   9 recaptures 8

134

PROBLEM  TO PLAY

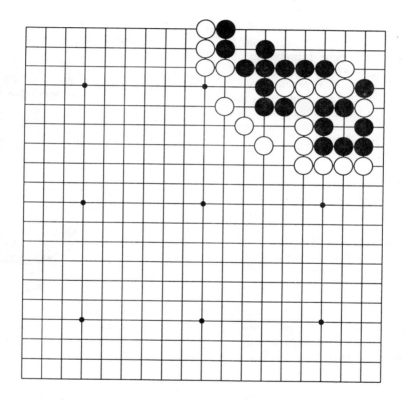

Each of black's groups must live independently. However, those two groups of living stones are to close to each other, and that is the problem.

Where should white begin operations? No matter what shape results, making ko represents success.

(8% respondent success rate)

Solution

A Two-step Ko

Solution Diagram There is no move at white's disposal to attack black's stones on the upper side, other than to hane at 1. And then, when black blocks at 2, white probes black's response by making the placement at 3. If black answers with the move at 4, at that point white plays the moves from 5 through 9, gaining impetus from the attack on the right side to threaten the upper side. In the end, a two-step ko is produced after 11, and this is the correct solution. In the middle of this variation, if black uses the move at 10 to connect at 5, white plays at **a**, killing black, since if black answers at 10, white plays at **b**.

Diagram 1 (A direct ko) When white makes the placement at 3, defending with 4 causes black to suffer a loss. White fixes the shape with the move at 5, and with the moves through 9 a direct ko is produced. It goes without saying that the two-step ko in the **Solution Diagram** is more advantageous for black than this direct ko.

Diagram 2 (Black is badly off) Also, when white plays at 1 & 3, the cut of black 4 is no good either. White plays atari at 5 and descends to 7. If black defends at 8, with the moves from white 9 through 13, black's group on the upper side is dead. If black plays 8 at 11 in order to make life, white plays at 8 to create a direct ko.

Diagram 3 (Failure) If white simply plays the placement of 1, turning at black 2 sets up a good defense. If white plays at 3, black 4 makes life for the group. In addition, if white plays 1 as a move at **a**, black descends to **b**, and white has no other move to use against black's groups.

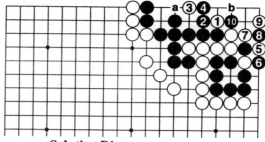

Solution Diagram   11 takes at 5

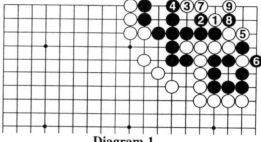

Diagram 1

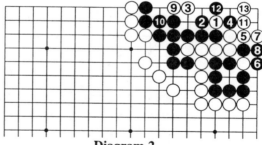

Diagram 2

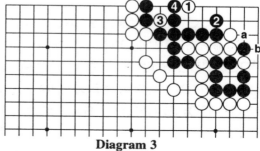

Diagram 3

136

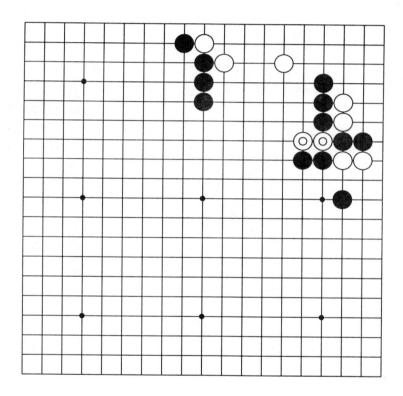

The shape here seems like one that often arises in handicap games. One wonders how black is to handle the two marked white stones, but while reading out the variations, one must not give up in midstream.

(44% respondent success rate)

Solution

The Ladder Turns Out to be Good for Black

Solution Diagram The atari of black 1 is the only move. In actuality, with this white is put into extremely difficult straits. If white tries to move out with a move at **a**, black plays at **b**, and to the extent that white moves out with this group, white's loss will become all the more painful, as everything will be captured. In other words, the ladder is good. If this was a real game, white would probably play something like a move at **c** or **d**, etc.

Diagram 1 (The ladder) The marked white stones do not perform a role as ladder breakers. If white moves out with the moves following white 2, black pursues the ladder with 3 & 5, and then at the point of the move at 15, black changes course and plays atari from the other direction. In the end, the ladder materializes with the moves through black 21.

Diagram 2 (Failing to read deeply enough) If black prematurely judges that the marked white stones do in fact work as ladder breakers, then the way that black would probably deal with the situation is by playing atari with 1 & 3, and then boxing white's stones in with the move at 5. By doing so, black manages to take control of the upper side with the move at 9, making good shape that is in general a credible outcome, but of course this result is not superior to the **Solution Diagram**.

Diagram 3 (Even worse for black) After playing atari at 1, boxing white in immediately with black 3 is the worst thing to do. The white stones on the upper side still have a great deal of potential to make trouble [aji].

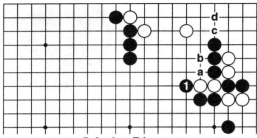

Solution Diagram

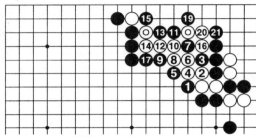

Diagram 1   18 connects

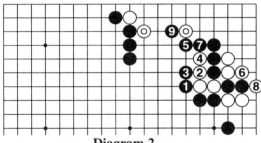

Diagram 2

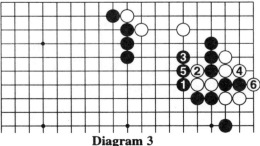

Diagram 3

138

PROBLEM **Reading** NUMBER 67 **WHITE** TO PLAY

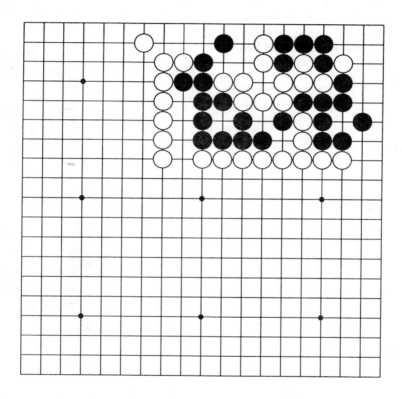

Neither the white nor the black stones which are entwined in the struggle have two definite eyes. Please demonstrate the strongest continuation for both sides.

It is unreasonable for white to engage black in a race to capture (semeai) directly.

(12% respondent success rate)

Solution

The Best Result is for Both Sides to Live

Solution Diagram First, white fixes the shape in the corner with the moves at 1 & 3, and then playing the diagonal move at 5 illustrates the first point in this problem. Black 6 is played to defend against black throwing in a stone at **a**, but then the placement of white 7 is a skillful finesse [tesuji] that encompasses the main point here. If one can work out the analysis to this stage, the rest is easy. Playing black 8 through 12 follows the correct order of moves whereby both sides end up living.

Diagram 1 (The ko fight) When white plays the diagonal move at 5, if black refuses to back down and plays at 6 instead, white throws in at 7 and the moves through black 10 lead to the ko fight. However, in regards to this ko, white has a perfect ko threat in the area at 11 which must be answered, showing up black's play as being unreasonable. In short, since black 6 must be used to make the defensive move at **a**, the effectiveness of white's moves at 1 & 3 is demonstrated.

Diagram 2 (White suffers a loss) After black plays at 6, the wedging insertion into black's position with white 7 also allows white to live, but the sequence through 12 ends with black making greater profit.

Diagram 3 (White loses the capturing race) If white neglects to set up play first in the corner, and simply plays the diagonal move at 1, black replies at 2, and though white gets the opportunity to then play in the corner at 3, black fills in one of white's liberties with the move at 4, and white's attack does not proceed quickly enough.

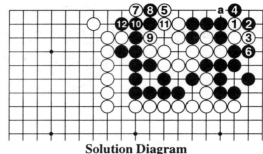

Solution Diagram

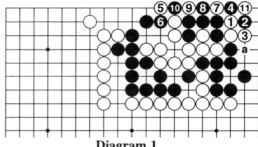

Diagram 1

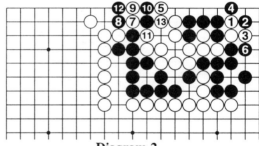

Diagram 2

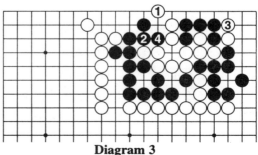

Diagram 3

PROBLEM (Reading NUMBER 68) WHITE TO PLAY

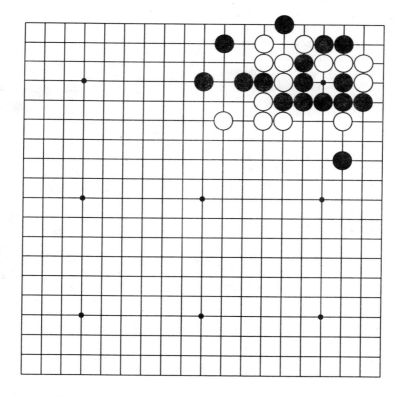

White has no chance to win the race to capture (semeai) in the corner. In that case, there is only one way of playing, but before doing so, how must one settle the shape in the corner? One must also be cognizant of black's possible responses.

(18% respondent success rate)

Solution

Wrap Black Up with the Proper Order of Moves

Solution Diagram Even if in this situation the capturing race [semeai] in the corner cannot be won, it is essential to expand the number of white's liberties to the greatest extent possible. First white fixes the shape with the moves at 1 & 3, the significance of which is that black is prevented from directly filling white's liberties. Consequently, with the forcing moves [kikashi] from 5 through 9, white can seal up black's group in sente. If white simply plays 1 at 5, black's move at **a** makes 7 & 9 ineffective as forcing moves.

Diagram 1 (Black incurs a loss) When white plays at 5, if black hanes at 6, the result is that black ends up having to capture white's stones with 8 & 10, so this variation is inferior to the one black plays in the **Solution Diagram**.

Diagram 2 (A ko fight) In addition to the variations given, if black hanes at 6 here, white gets to connect at 7, leaving black badly off. If black connects underneath at 10, white starts the ko fight with 11, and white has the moves at 13 & 15 available to play in exchange for the ko. If the prospect of a ko fight is distasteful to black, the move at 10 may be played at 11, but then white extends to 10 and is well off.

Diagram 3 (A one move difference) The connection of white 1 is a weak and ineffective move. When white plays the move at 3 next, black's reply at **a** can be omitted altogether in favor of filling in a liberty at 4. This produces a one move difference as compared to the variation given in the **Solution Diagram**.

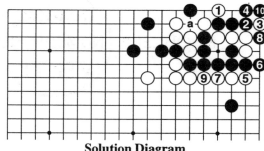

Solution Diagram

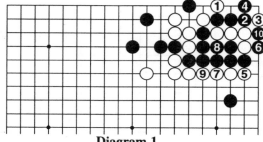

Diagram 1

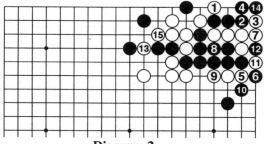

Diagram 2

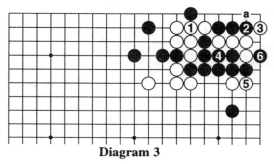

Diagram 3

142

Reading

PROBLEM **NUMBER 69**

BLACK TO PLAY

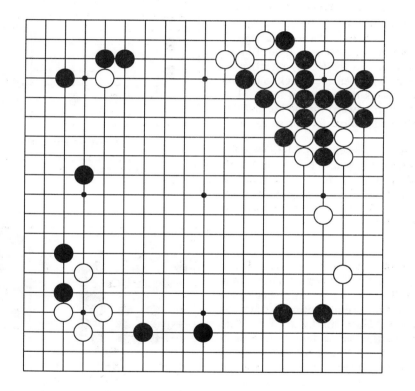

The upper right corner is still in the throes of battle. In this board position, please work out a continuation likely to occur in a real game through to a lull in the action.

Best moves for both sides will produce ko, but one must not be lax in determining the status of ko threats.

(18% respondent success rate)

143

Solution

Black Plays to Make Ko and Win it

Solution Diagram Whatever else black does, without playing at 1 to capture white's two stones, there is no way to survive. It is natural for white to play atari at 2, and then play 4 as a throw-in. When white defends in the corner at 6, black extends at 7, and an inevitable sequence of moves through 17 allow black to engineer a ko fight. Black's trump card here is the locally effective ko threat at 19, which enables black to win the ko. White plays the moves at 22 & 24 in exchange [furi-kawari] for the ko, and this may be considered par for this situation.

Within this variation, if white uses the move at 6 to atari at **a**, it leaves black with the local ko threat at **b**, and therefore is a bad move. Also, if white plays 12 at **c**, by answering at **d**, black gets even more ko material to use.

Diagram 1 (Black loses the ko) If the move at black 9 in the **Solution Diagram** is played as the atari at 1 here, the shape ends up being fixed, representing failure for black. Even if black attacks at 3 & 5, white sets the variation on a different course with the moves at 6 & 8. The following moves through black 19 lead to another ko, but when white plays at 22, there is no continuation available to black.

Diagram 2 (No ko at all) Throwing a stone in at black 1 is not a ko threat at all whatsoever. White responds by connecting at 2, and when black captures at 3, white plays at 4 and black is completely annihilated.

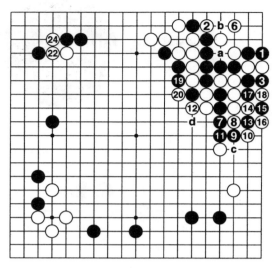

Solution Diagram

4: throw-in; 5: captures; 21: takes ko at 15; 23 takes at 13

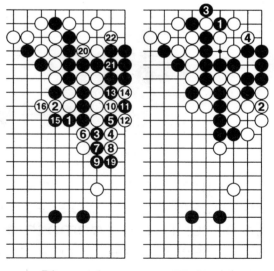

Diagram 1

17 takes ko; 18 connects at 5

Diagram 2

PROBLEM **Reading NUMBER 70 WHITE TO PLAY**

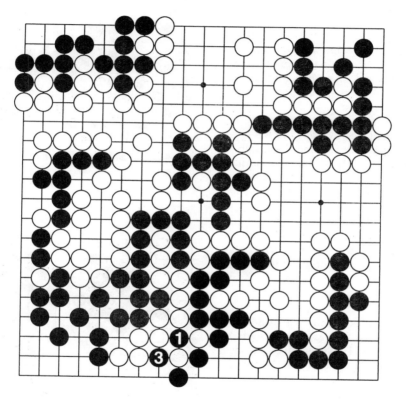

The theme of this problem is exchange in a ko fight.
Here black takes and then wins the ko with 1 & 3.
Well then, white will at the same time get the moves of 2 &
4 elsewhere in exchange for losing the ko. Where is the
biggest place to play those moves?

(72% respondent success rate)

Solution

The Upper Left Corner is Worth 38 Points

Solution Diagram The life and death of both side's large group of stones on the lower side depend on the outcome of the ko fight there, so this is an all-or-nothing ko, in which no ko threat will be answered. Therefore, black plays 1 & 3 dissolving the ko. As compensation, white is invited to play two moves anywhere on the board deemed desirable, and of course white must be careful to choose the biggest place on the board to play those moves.

The correct place to play is in the upper left corner, and white captures black's stones there with 2 & 4. This is the biggest place on the board, an area of considerable size that is worth 38 points to white.

Capturing black's ten stones in the center by cutting at **a** & **b** is worth about 29 points. Compared to the correct line of play, white loses approximately 10 points this way.

Diagram 1 (Black is alive) If white could kill this corner with 2 & 4, that would be the biggest move. However, black will then hane at 5, and play atari at 7, a skillful maneuver to survive [shinogi] that only costs black four sacrifice stones.

Diagram 2 (Overconcentration) The moves at white 2 & 4 on the left side seem to be big, but that is in appearance only. The point is that regardless of an exchange that results from the ko, white can always use the technique of playing at **a**, black **b**, and white **c** to start a ko fight here.

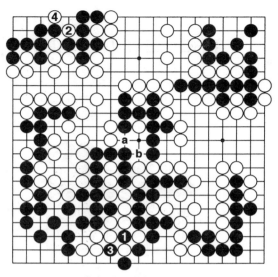

Solution Diagram

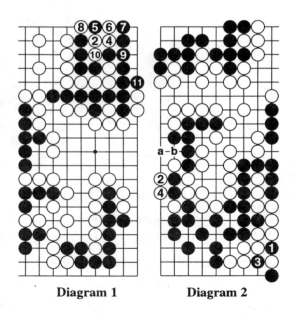

Diagram 1   Diagram 2

146

Race to Capture [Semeai]

PROBLEM NUMBER 71

WHITE TO PLAY

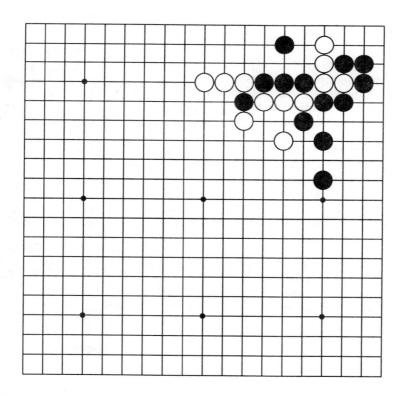

An artless direct attack will not succeed.

White's first move must strike at the vital point, but black has resources to put up stiff resistance.

(16% respondent success rate)

Solution

The Best that can be Done is to Make Ko

Solution Diagram In this situation, neither side's group of stones have eyes. The ironclad rule that holds in capturing races [semeai] such as these is that one must start filling liberties from the outside. If one starts filling liberties on the inside in this shape, there is no way to win.

The attachment of white 1 is the vital point here. It is such a strong move that one might assume that this blow alone would put black in an impossible predicament, but that is not the case. Black forces with 2 to fix the shape, then the diagonal move at black 4 is a strong move that offers stubborn resistance. The moves following white 5 are precisely made in the correct move order, and lead to ko after white 11. This is the correct solution. In this sequence, if white plays 5 at 8, black plays at 11 and wins the race to capture.

Diagram 1 (Black loses) After fixing the shape with the move at 2, drawing back to black 4 makes bad shape. After first playing hane at 5, white pushes through at 7, and black does not have a viable response to play.

Diagram 2 (Black loses) Simply drawing back to black 2 ends in the same way. With the moves at 3 & 5, white wins. This is conclusive proof that the attachment of white 1 is the vital point.

Diagram 3 (Failure for white) The hane of white 1 here appears to fill in a liberty, but it actually is bad form. By letting black answer at 2, even if white plays at 3, black 4 has white paralyzed.

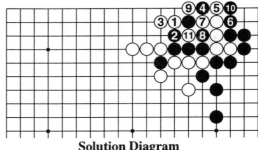

Solution Diagram

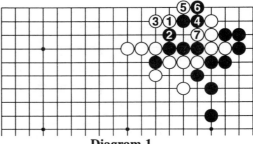

Diagram 1

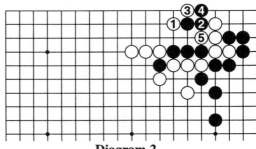

Diagram 2

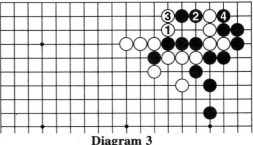

Diagram 3

Race to Capture [Semeai]

PROGRAM **NUMBER 72**

WHITE TO PLAY

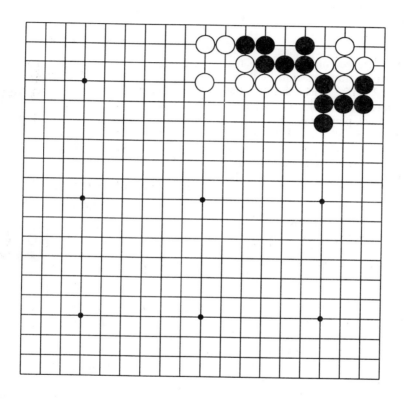

The black stones seem to have more liberties, and the potential eye shape of the group encouraging. It looks like white has no hope in winning the race to capture (semeai), but the special properties of the corner will allow white to put up winning resistance.

(12% respondent success rate)

Solution

White 1 & 3 Make Good Form

Solution Diagram If one tries to directly precipitate a capturing race [semeai] in this shape, there is no hope of winning. Before initiating such an action, one must reinforce the shape to make it more stubbornly resistant to capture.

Playing the diagonal move of white 1 is the way to start resisting tenaciously. When black plays at 2, white 3 occupies the vital shape. Now it is not a simple matter to capture white. If black plays at 4, white makes the placement of 5, followed in the correct move order by white 7. Up to 12, the position becomes ko. Along the way, if black plays 10 at **a**, white replies at 11, and the position becomes ko.

Diagram 1 (Double ko) If white 7 in the **Solution Diagram** is played as the hane at 1 here, a bad result is produced. With the moves from black 2 through 6, the position turns into a double ko for black. White is lost.

Diagram 2 (Black 2 is the vital point) If white hurries to attempt to win the race to capture by playing the diagonal move at 1 directly, black lands a sharp blow with the placement of 2 at the vital point. Now, no matter what moves white plays following this, or how stubbornly resists, white is fated to lose the race to capture between the groups by one move.

Diagram 3 (Again, failure for white) At first sight, the placement of white 1 seems to be played at the vital point, but in this case the diagonal move of black 2 refutes it. Please confirm this for yourself.

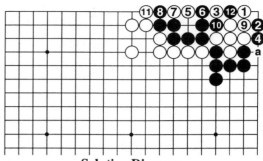

Solution Diagram

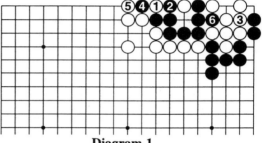

Diagram 1

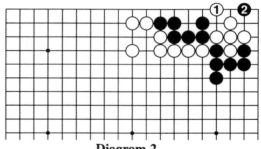

Diagram 2

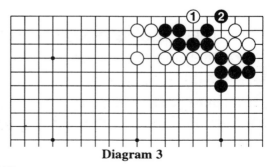

Diagram 3

150

Race to Capture [Semeai]
PROBLEM NUMBER 73
WHITE TO PLAY

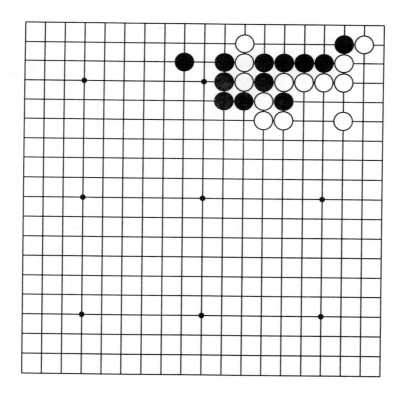

The shape is such that white cannot win the fight here unconditionally.

A ko may arise in various ways, but the important thing in this problem is which side gets to take the ko first. It is essential to consider black's strongest responses.

(8% respondent success rate)

Solution

Ko Results with Black Getting First Turn to Take it

Solution Diagram It is essential for white to turn at 1 and then hane at 3. Anything other than this would not produce a race to capture [semeai]. At this point, black connects at 4, the reply that offers the strongest resistance, but in response, the attachment of white 5 is a good move. If black plays atari at 6, what follows is an inevitable order of moves through 12 that leads to ko in the position where it is black's turn to capture. This is the correct solution. If, in this variation, white plays 3 at 4, black answers at 3 and white is lost.

Diagram 1 (A variation) After playing at 1 & 3, when white attaches at 5, the black hane in the corner at 6 will be answered by the throw-in at 7, and once again the position turns into ko with black getting the first turn to take it. If white uses the move at 7 to make the hanging connection in the corner at **a**, after black **b**, white **c**, and black **d**, white 7 leads to the same result.

Diagram 2 (White's turn to take the ko) In response to the attachment of white 5, challenging the ko directly at 6 is bad for black. White gets the opportunity to play at 7, taking the ko first.

Diagram 3 (Worst case scenario for black) When white plays the moves at 1 & 3, blocking at 4 is the worst thing that black could do. White not only takes profit by capturing at 5, the position also ends up with a ko fight in which it is white's turn to capture first.

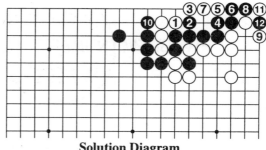

Solution Diagram

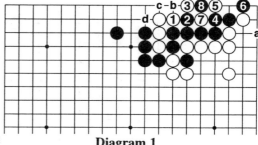

Diagram 1

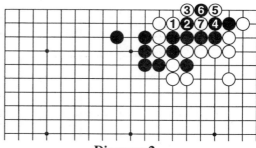

Diagram 2

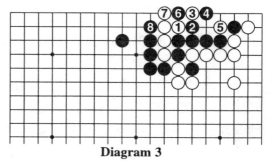

Diagram 3

152

Race to Capture [Semeai]
PROBLEM NUMBER 74
WHITE TO PLAY

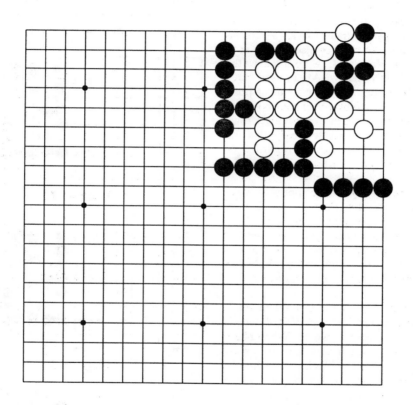

This is quite a formidable problem. Even though the first move is obvious, the continuation is difficult. Simply settling for a sequence to make ko represents failure.

(2% respondent success rate)

Solution

White 3 is an Exquisite Move

Solution Diagram If white does not make the placement at 1, the will be no race to capture [semeai] here. In response, black 2 puts up the stiffest resistance, but at this point the diagonal move of white 3 is exquisite. The upshot is that this one move simultaneously frustrates black's aim of either starting a ko fight or else cutting at **a**. When black plays at 4, white 5 leaves the corner with only one eye. After this, if black plays at **b**, white's reply at **c** creates a position that has the semblance of a ko, but there are so many approach moves that black must make to threaten white seriously, that the situation should perhaps be regarded as unconditional life for white.

Diagram 1 (A one move approach move ko for black) If white defends against a cut at **a** in a simple-minded manner by playing at 3, with the moves at 4 & 6, black sets up a one move approach move ko. The difference between this result and the **Solution Diagram** is as great as day and night.

Diagram 2 (A direct ko) When black plays the wedging insertion of 2, descending to white 3 is even worse. When black cuts at 4, the position now turns into a direct ko. Of course, if black joins white in blundering and instead of playing at 4, plays at 5, white throws in at 7, taking away black's eyes.

Diagram 3 (Black cannot connect underneath) When white plays at 1, the hane at 2 will not enable black to connect underneath on the upper side. Wedging into black's position with the skillful forcing move [kikashi] at white 3 settles matters with a single blow.

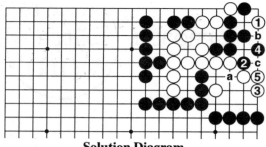

Solution Diagram

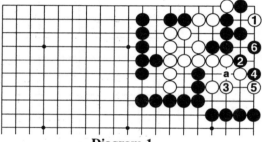

Diagram 1

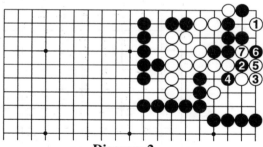

Diagram 2

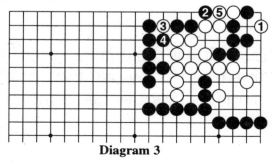

Diagram 3

154

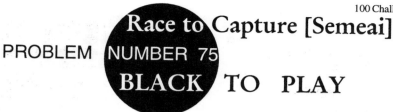

Race to Capture [Semeai]

PROBLEM NUMBER 75

BLACK TO PLAY

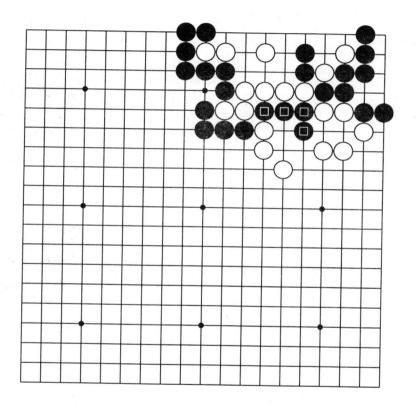

The four marked black stones in the center have only three liberties, so there is no time to waste in the race to capture (semeai).

Therefore, it is obvious where one must play next to take white's liberties, but crude reading afterward will fail.

(42% respondent success rate)

155

Solution

Making Ko is the Strongest Measure

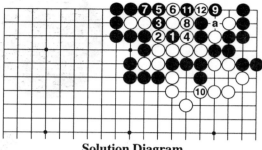

Solution Diagram

Solution Diagram In order to restrict the number of liberties of white's group to not more than three, wedging into the position with black 1 is the only move. When white plays at 2, making the throw-in at black 3 is also essential. Then, the play that follows the capture at white 4 illustrates the main point of this problem. With the moves from the descent to black 5 through 9, both sides play the strongest skillful finesse [tesuji] to turn the position into ko, and this is the correct solution. Amid this variation, if black plays 5 at 7, or plays black 9 at **a**, black loses the race to capture [semeai] in both cases. Please confirm this for yourself.

The following diagrams will show that white's responses here are the strongest ones available.

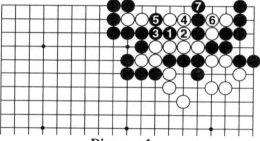

Diagram 1

Diagram 1 (Defending on the other side) First, when black plays at 1, answering on the opposite side at white 2 allows black to connect at 3, and after black plays at 7, white cannot play atari against black's three stones on either side, and loses the race to capture.

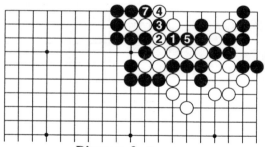

Diagram 2   6 connects

Diagram 2 (Capturing on the other side) When black throws in at 3, if white captures on this side, playing atari at black 5 and filling in another of white's liberties with 7 is simplicity itself.

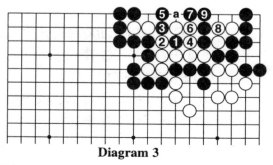

Diagram 3

Diagram 3 (No atari to play) And then, when black plays at 5, if white refrains from playing atari at **a**, and simply plays 6, black plays the moves at 7 & 9, and white once again is unable to play atari on either side due to a shortage of liberties.

Race to Capture [Semeai]

PROBLEM NUMBER 76

BLACK TO PLAY

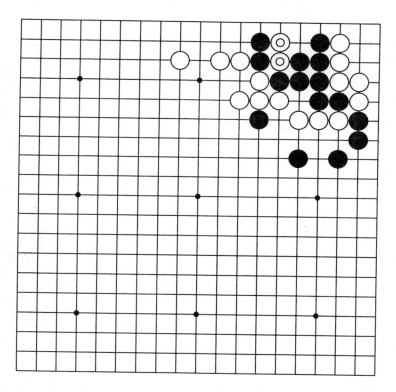

If black rushes to take the two marked white stones, black will not only be unable to make life, but will also lose any advantage in the race to capture (semeai).

This problem challenges one to find the correct move order to attack the white stones in the corner.

(22% respondent success rate)

Solution

Make a One Move Approach Move Ko

Solution Diagram This is quite a difficult problem, so it is marvelous that the respondent success rate was 22%.

When black hanes at 1, if white plays at 2, there is no other option for black but to eat into the corner with the move at 3. The idea behind capturing with white 4 is to create a position where white has an eye and black does not, in which case black is simply dead, but black fills white's liberties with 5 & 7, and with the moves through 12, a one move approach move ko develops. This is the correct solution to the problem. The fact that white cannot play atari at **a** directly is acutely painful.

Diagram 1 (Black loses) After the exchange of black 1 for white 2, capturing white's two stones with the move at 3 will not enable black to win the race to capture [semeai]. White plays 6 through 20, the strongest sequence of moves here. After this, if black plays at **a**, white can hang tough by connecting at 1, and the shape is such that black has no move to make.

Diagram 2 (A direct ko) When black plays at 1, blocking at 2 incurs a loss for white. The connection of black 3 makes it necessary for white to play at 4, so with the following moves through 7 a direct ko is created.

Diagram 3 (Three move approach move ko) Starting with the attachment of 3 is no good for black. With the moves from white 2 through 14, a position arises in which black is forced to play a three move approach move ko.

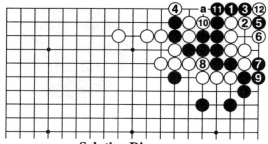

Solution Diagram

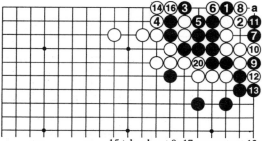

Diagram 1   15 takes ko at 9; 17 connects at 12; 18: throw-in below 3; 19 captures

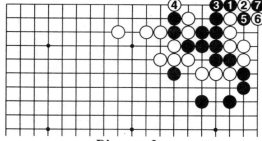

Diagram 2

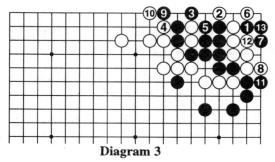

Diagram 3

158

1

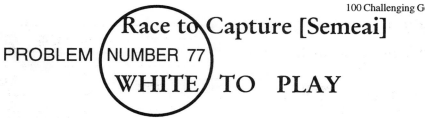

Race to Capture [Semeai]

PROBLEM NUMBER 77

WHITE TO PLAY

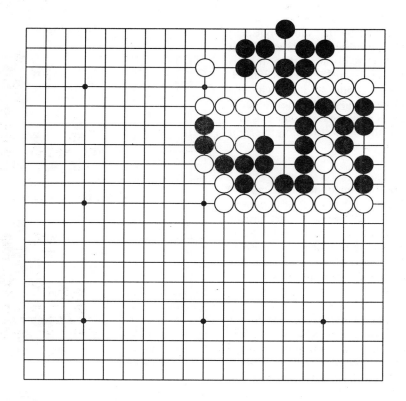

Can black's twelve stones in the center be captured or not? The key is to find out how to extend the liberties of the white group in the corner.

Please concentrate on this one isolated question and find the solution.

(13% respondent success rate)

Solution

Bad Shape Makes an Exquisite Move

Solution Diagram The empty triangle created by white 1 makes bad shape, but is the first step towards the correct solution. When black attaches at 2, it seems as though there is no way at all that white's liberties could be extended by that move, but next white 3 is a good move that is a little bit difficult to visualize ahead of time. It frees white from all difficulties. After this, if black plays at 4, white replies at 5 and wins the race to capture [semeai] by one move. If black plays 4 at **a**, white responds at 4, taking control of the black group on the right side and capturing it.

Diagram 1 (A ko fight) After the exchange of white 1 for black 2, it is premature to play the placement of white 3, rushing too quickly ahead. Black has the tenacious moves of 4 & 6 to make ko, and besides the outside ko threat of 8, black has further ko material to use at **a** and **b**.

Diagram 2 (A ko that black wins) Jumping to 1 will not extend white's liberties. Black wedges into the vital point with 2, and all at once white's liberties have filled up. Playing ko with white 7 is unreasonable, since black has ko material at 8 and the following moves.

Diagram 3 (The same result) If white 3 in the previous diagram is played at 3 here, a different variation is produced but the result is the same. There will be no way in the world that black's stones surrounded by white in the center will be captured.

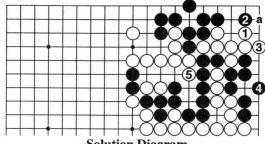

Solution Diagram

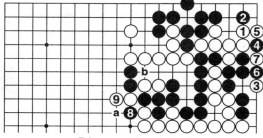

Diagram 1   10 takes ko

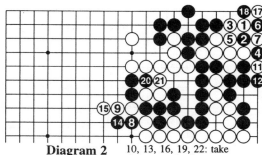

Diagram 2   10, 13, 16, 19, 22: take their respective ko

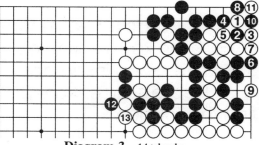

Diagram 3   14 takes ko

160

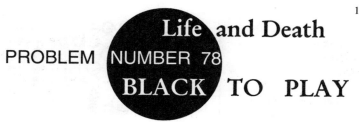

Life and Death

PROBLEM NUMBER 78

BLACK TO PLAY

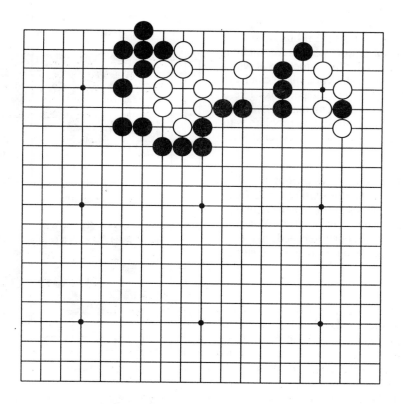

If one just discovers the first move here, the vital point, then the problem is an easy one. However, if one jumps to the hasty conclusion that it is too easy, one will fail.

It is vital that one carry through with one's reading and not halt midway through.

(22% respondent success rate)

Solution

White's Stones Die Unconditionally

Solution Diagram There is something of a booby trap lurking in this problem, but if one reads very carefully, things will go smoothly without that being a factor. The placement of black 1 occupies the vital point, but regardless of that fact, if black does not start the attack against white here, nothing will develop at all. Since blocking at white 2 is the only possible reply, black can hane at 3 and cut at 5. The shape looks like a simple ko, but considering that the solution is incorrect. The point of this problem is to be found in the continuation. After this...

Diagram 1 (White dies unconditionally) Without playing ko, the atari of black 7 and the crawling moves at 9 & 11 make up the technique to use in this situation. With the moves through 15, black succeeds magnificently in annihilating all of white's stones unconditionally.

Diagram 2 (White lives) After first making the placement at 1, if black descends to 3, and then plays the move at 5, white is permitted to answer with the move at 6 to insure the life of the group. At 3, if black pushes down at 6 instead, white **a** causes black's stones to be caught in a shortage of liberties.

Diagram 3 (The vital point) Playing the attachment of black 1 allows white to take the vital point with 2 and live. Besides this, whether black plays at **a**, **b**, or **c**, white responds at the vital point of 2.

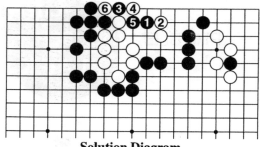

Solution Diagram

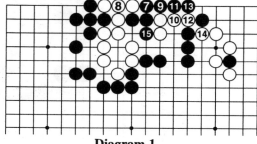

Diagram 1

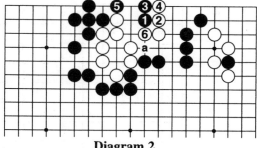

Diagram 2

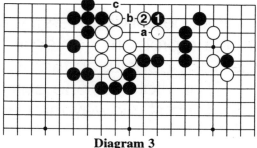

Diagram 3

162

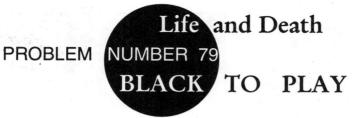

Life and Death

PROBLEM NUMBER 79

BLACK TO PLAY

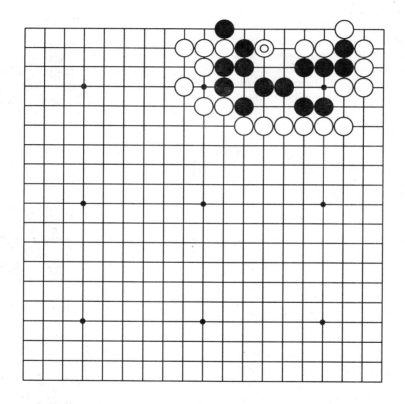

Unless black can capture the marked white stone, the group cannot live.

Making the position into ko is a failure. Please work out a sequence that permits the black group to live unconditionally.

(30% respondent success rate)

Solution

A Calm and Collected Connection

Solution Diagram In order to capture white's marked stone, there is no other measure to use than to start by wedging in at black 1. It is natural for white to defend at 2, but connecting at black 3 here is a good move, calm and collected. With it, black guarantees life for the group, unconditionally. Following this, if white captures at 4, black throws a stone in at 5, and then 7 sets up a simple case of rapidly disappearing liberties to capture at least two white stones.

Diagram 1 (A variation) When black plays 1 & 3, if white opts for a variation and connects at 4, it is good enough for black to connect at 5. If white replies at 6, black plays at 7, and here too, white is not able to link up with the marked stone to save it.

Diagram 2 (A ko fight) Playing the throw-in at black 3 prematurely changes the nature of the position entirely. White captures at 4, and now the connection of black 5 is met with the move at 6, with which white hangs tough to produce a ko fight.

Diagram 3 (Another ko fight) With the moves at 1 & 3, black clearly sets out from the start to turn the position into a ko fight. The intention behind black 7 is to create a double ko here [if white plays a ko threat elsewhere here, then comes back to capture at 4, black 7 makes a double ko], but white squelches that scheme by capturing at 10. [The position is now a direct ko: black captures at 7, and the ko fight starts. Black will next capture at 5 to win the ko, or white will ignore a ko threat and fill at 7 to win.]

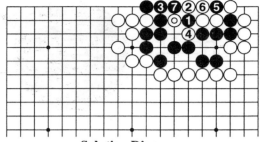

Solution Diagram

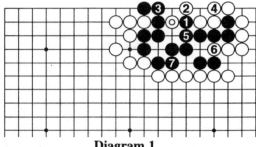

Diagram 1

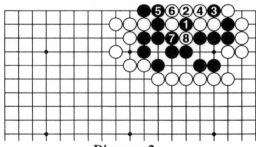

Diagram 2

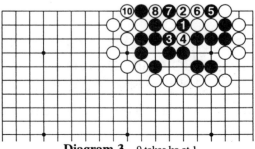

Diagram 3 9 takes ko at 1

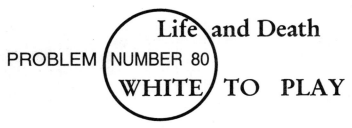

Life and Death
PROBLEM NUMBER 80
WHITE TO PLAY

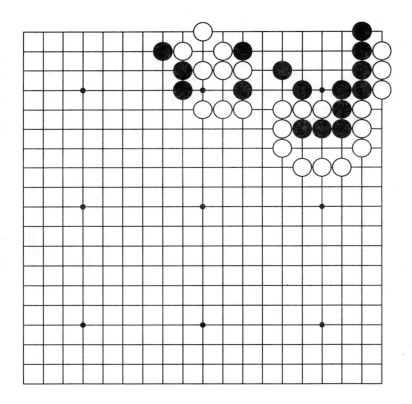

There is a lot of open space in the shape of black's group. Should white play inside that group, or attack it from the outside? If one can make ko here, one succeeds.

(4% respondent success rate)

165

Solution

Aim at Starting a Ko Fight

Solution Diagram Black's shape here is overly spacious, so if white attacks from the inside it will not go well. Going so far as to attack at white 1, working from the outside in, is the skillful finesse [tesuji] to use here. The best way to answer this is for black to expand the space inside the group as much as possible with 2 & 4. But the attachment at the vital point at white 5 forces a crisis within the position, whether black likes it or not. When white plays the move at 9, black fills in white's liberties from the back with 10 & 12, and after 13, a direct ko is produced.

Diagram 1 (Black dies) When white plays 1 & 3, descending to 4 does not make enough room in the group's shape. After pushing in at white 5, the simple placement of 7 makes this a five point oversized eye [nakade], and black dies.

Diagram 2 (Double ko) After white 1, the counterattack of black 2 is answered by white drawing back at 3 and then cutting at 5 & 7. With the moves through black 10, at first sight the position seems to have turned into a ko fight, but by descending to white 9 and throwing in at 13, a double ko is creating. Black is annihilated.

Diagram 3 (Failure for white) Pushing in at white 1 and then attacking from the inside with the placement at 3 is unreasonable. With the moves from 5 through 11, white aims at making this another five point oversized eye, but by playing the move at 14, black makes life for the group. Notice how the marked black stone works perfectly here.

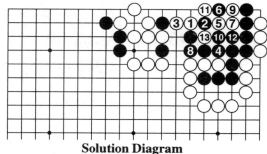

Solution Diagram

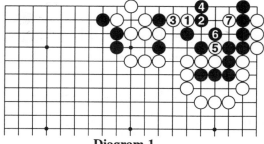

Diagram 1

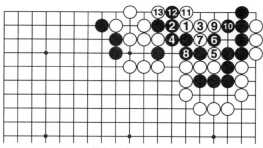

Diagram 2

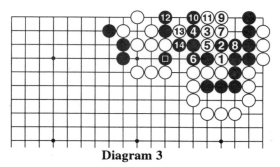

Diagram 3

166

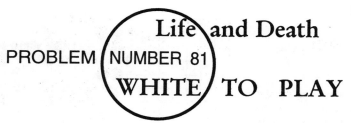

Life and Death
PROBLEM NUMBER 81
WHITE TO PLAY

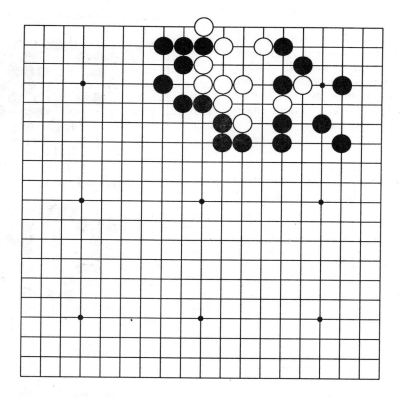

The sequence that one is called to find is a long one, but it is cut-and-dried. The route to make life is easily found out.

With a respondent success rate above 70%, this problem tops the list.

(71% respondent success rate)

Solution

A Straightforward Variation Leads to Ko

Solution Diagram In this problem and others like it, the essential thing is that one resolutely fix the shape where it must be fixed, forcing where one must, in this case attacking black's weak points.

Playing the moves from white 1 & 3, through black 4 is natural. At this point, plunging ahead with the throw-in of white 5 follows good form in the only way that it seems that good form is possible, and the continuation through black 10 is also natural. Then, after white hanes at 11...

Diagram 1 (A ko fight) From the cut at black 12 through 22, a straightforward variation leads to a ko fight, and this is the correct solution.

Along the way, if black 12 is played as a hane at 20, the capture at white **a** is sente, so white can then make a throw-in at 13, creating a case of rapidly disappearing liberties to capture at least five of black's stones.

Diagram 2 (An improper move order) After fixing the shape with the moves through white 3, immediately playing the hane of 5 ends in failure. When black gets to connect at 6, white has no follow-up continuation.

Diagram 3 (Failure for white) Poking at white 1 is also a move that merely helps the opponent. Black connects at 2, and when white plays at 3, black 4 settles matters.

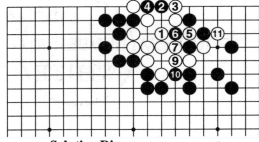

Solution Diagram 8 connects at 5

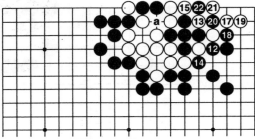

Diagram 1 16 connects

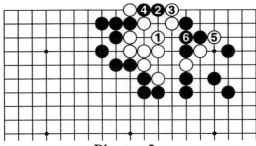

Diagram 2

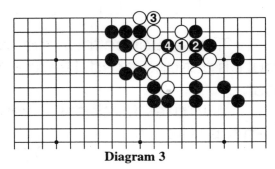

Diagram 3

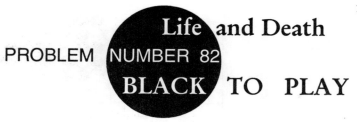

Life and Death

PROBLEM NUMBER 82

BLACK TO PLAY

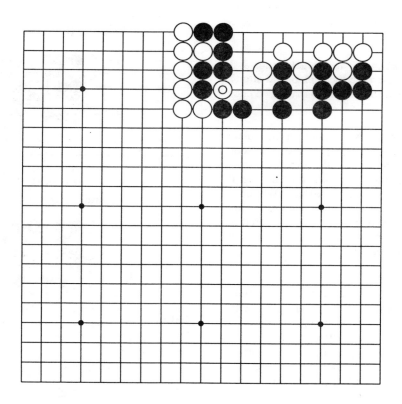

Discovering where to play the first move is the most important item on the agenda.

If one is too clumsy in pressing the attack, the marked white stone will come to play a significant role.

(28% respondent success rate)

Solution

Poke at the Vital Point

Solution Diagram Black pokes from the reverse side at the vital point with 1. One may feel reluctant to deliberately force a solid connection at a place where there was the possibility of saddling the opponent with a false eye, but this one move completely severs white's lifeline.

If white connects at 2, black hanes at 3. White 4 is answered by black 5, and after 7, white is left with no way to make two eyes.

Diagram 1 (A variation) When black pokes at 1, if white descends to 2, black cuts into white's position with 3, adding a stone to the first before sacrificing them both in accordance with the go proverb. White has only one eye in the corner, and as for the position to the left, white 8 is answered by black 9 & 10, moves that settle the question without any worries.

Diagram 2 (A blind spot) One may think that by jumping to black 1, white is left without a way to make two eyes, but when black plays at 3, the connection of white 4 is a good move that secures the life of the group [shinogi]. Even if black plays 5 and the following moves, white plays atari with 8 and the marked white stone is found to work effectively in this situation.

Diagram 3 (Failure for black) Playing the hane of 1 also fails for black. With 2 and the moves that follow, white takes advantage of black's shortage of liberties to end up occupying the vital point at 6, making life for the group.

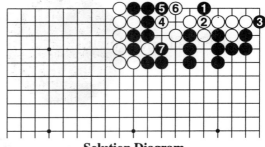

Solution Diagram

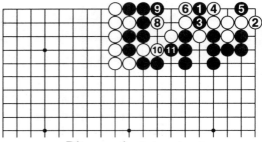

Diagram 1 7: throw-in at 3

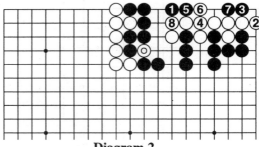

Diagram 2

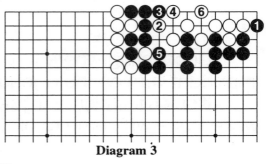

Diagram 3

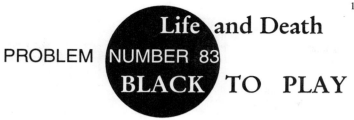

Life and Death

PROBLEM NUMBER 83

BLACK TO PLAY

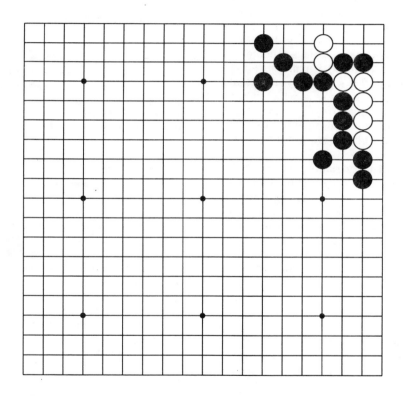

The two black stones in the corner have three liberties. In principle, black cannot win a race to capture (semeai) by playing in a straightforward manner, but by using the special properties of the corner, the way is made clear.

(6% respondent success rate)

Solution

"Strange Things Happen at the 2-1 Point"

Solution Diagram As a vital point in the corner, the go proverb states that: "Strange things happen at the 2-1 point," and the shape here does not offer an exception to this rule. The diagonal move at black 1 is the first step towards the solution. If white plays at 2 & 4 in order to fill black's liberties, then even though black cannot win a race to capture [semeai], when white plays atari at 8, black 9 is a critically important move that creates a shape in which white has a five point oversized eye [nakade]. This is a dead shape. Now, if white tries to make a second eye at **a**, black **b** is a good response.

Diagram 1 (A variation) When black plays the move at 3, one must treat white's throw-in at 4 here with careful attention. The fact is, black can then make the placement of 5, and with this single blow, black now wins the capturing race. If black mistakenly uses the move at 5 to capture at **a**, white blocks at 5 and all of a sudden a ko develops. [That would be a direct ko for black and a one move approach move ko for white.]

Diagram 2 (Another ko fight) Even though it appears that turning at 1 increases black's liberties, the attachment of white 2 at the vital point makes a ko fight unavoidable.

Diagram 3 (White lives) Blocking at 1 is the worst thing that black could do. After making the placement at 2, white plays at 4, and with this bolt out of the blue, black's liberties are filled in quickly, allowing white to live unconditionally.

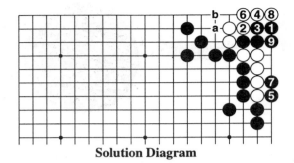

Solution Diagram

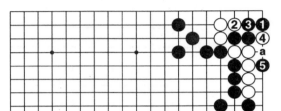

Diagram 1

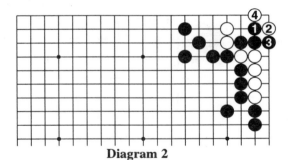

Diagram 2

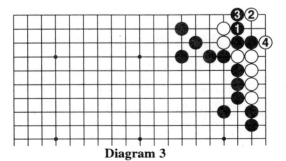

Diagram 3

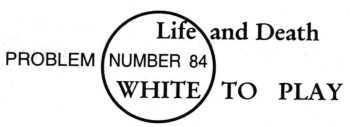

Life and Death
PROBLEM NUMBER 84
WHITE TO PLAY

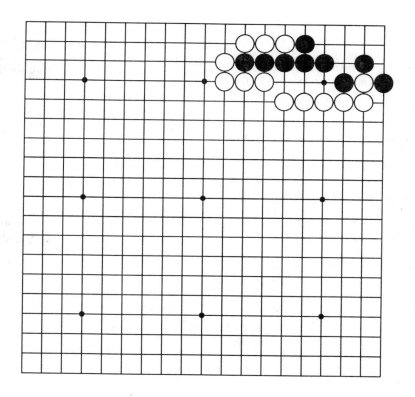

It is clear where to play the first move, but it is the play afterward that is central to the problem.

Black has techniques available to fight back, and the group will not die unconditionally.

(29% respondent success rate)

Solution

The Best that can be Done is to Make Ko

Solution Diagram The placement of white 1 starts the attack in a way that few would find fault with. Then the block of black 2 is the only move. At that point, playing the hane of white 3 and the diagonal move of white 5 follows the correct move order. In response, the connection of black 8 is the strongest move here. The sequence proceeds to the sacrificial move of black 10 and the throw-in of 12, whereupon a ko fight takes place, and this is the correct solution to the problem.

Diagram 1 (Black lives) After the exchange of white 1 for black 2, playing the diagonal move immediately at white 3 lets black descend at the vital point with 4. Even though white can connect underneath with 5, black 6 & 8 leave white no way to save the stone at 1. In other words, black's group lives unconditionally.

Diagram 2 (Cutting also ends in failure) Neither is it good to cut with white 3, since letting black connect at 4 means that things will not go well. When white plays at 5, black 6 is a good move. In the end, capturing the white stones with the bent four shape inside the corner assures black of life. If black plays 6 at 8, white replies at 6, black **a**, and then white plays at 7 to produce a ko fight.

Diagram 3 (Black dies) When white makes the placement at 1, it is not good for black to connect at 2. The moves through white 7 leave black with a dead, five point oversized eye shape [nakade]. If black 4 is played at **a**, white answers with **b**, black 4, and then white 5.

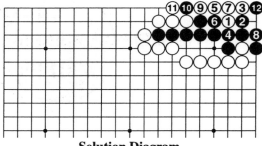

Solution Diagram

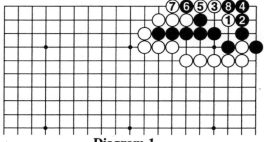

Diagram 1

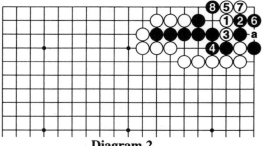

Diagram 2

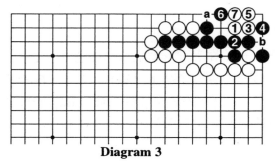

Diagram 3

174

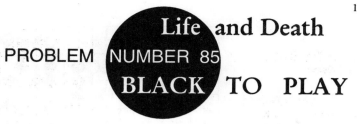

Life and Death

PROBLEM NUMBER 85

BLACK TO PLAY

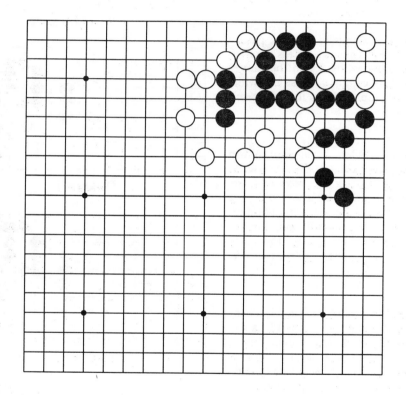

The diagram here takes up a quarter of the board, but the focal point is the corner. Attacking the white corner is related to the fact that black's group on the upper side is not alive yet.

(31% respondent success rate)

175

Solution

The Best Result is for Both Sides to Live

Solution Diagram The attachment of black 1 is played at the vital point of white's shape. Here, once again, the proverbial 2-1 point in the corner is occupied in good form, and the move works effectively.

When white extends to 2, black pushes through at 3, and white is helpless to resist. In the end, after white 4 and the moves through 8, black captures two stones while white also lives, and this is the best result for both.

Diagram 1 (White is captured) When black pushes through at 3, if white tries to hang tough by playing the move at 4, the placement of black 5 kills white with a single blow. If white then answers at 6, black plays at 7, while playing white 6 at **a** brings on black 6. There is no question that black is far ahead in any race to capture [semeai] here.

Diagram 2 (A ko fight) Fixing the shape step by step at a snail's pace with black 1 & 3 displays bad form. After this, even if black attaches at the vital point with 7, white is able to block black from connecting by playing at 8, and black has to hustle even to get a ko out of the situation. [White also has two good local ko threats below.]

Diagram 3 (A simple way to make ko) If it is a ko that black wants to play, attaching at 1 is a simple way to start it. If white plays 2 & 4, black gets a good result with the hane at 5.

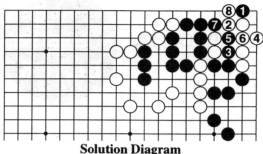

Solution Diagram

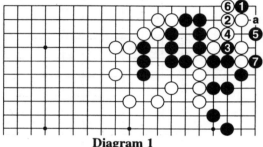

Diagram 1

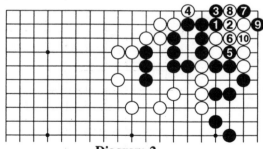

Diagram 2

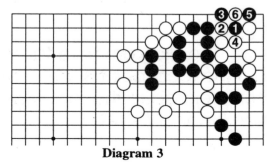

Diagram 3

176

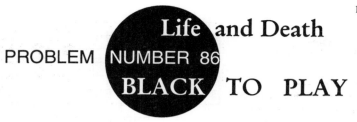

Life and Death

PROBLEM NUMBER 86

BLACK TO PLAY

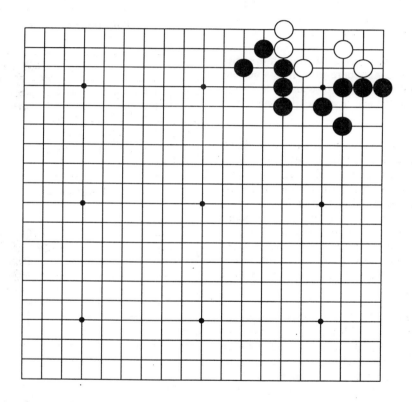

At first glance white's group in the corner appears to have plenty of room to make two eyes. How should one attack in order to make trouble?

If one misses playing the vital point with the first move, the group will end up living easily.

(46% respondent success rate)

Solution

A Placement Leads to Ko

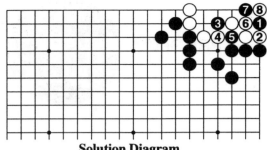

Solution Diagram

Solution Diagram The placement of black 1 at the 2-1 point on this side is the vital point. After exchanging this move for white 2, attaching across white's knight's move with black 3 is a skillful finesse [tesuji]. After white plays at 4, black is able to start a ko fight with 5 & 7.

Instead of playing at 2, should white somehow reply somewhere else in this corner, black will be allowed to connect at 2, and white has no chance to make life in any other manner.

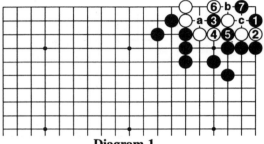

Diagram 1

Diagram 1 (White dies) When black plays at 5, white could only play atari against black's stone with the move at 6, thinking that it makes life for the group, as the result of an hallucination. When black plays the diagonal move at 7, white's group ends up unconditionally dead. If white now plays at **a**, black answers at **b**, and if white instead plays at **b**, black **a**; in either case, white is precluded from continuing with a move at **c**.

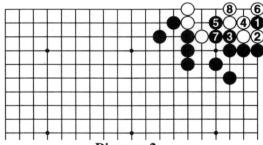

Diagram 2

Diagram 2 (Half of the group lives) After the exchange of black 1 and white 2, if black plays atari at 3, the sequence through white 8 leads to half of the group living. Naturally, in a real game situation, if the status of ko material across the board is not in black's favor, this is the variation that would be played.

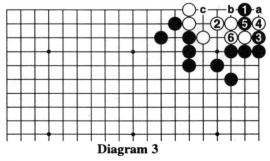

Diagram 3

Diagram 3 (White lives) The placement of black 1 here is played in bad form. After white defends at 2 through 6, if black next plays at **a**, white plays atari at **b**, followed by white **c**, making life for the group unconditionally.

178

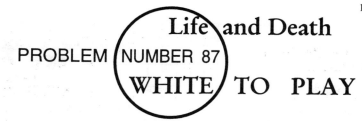

Life and Death

PROBLEM NUMBER 87

WHITE TO PLAY

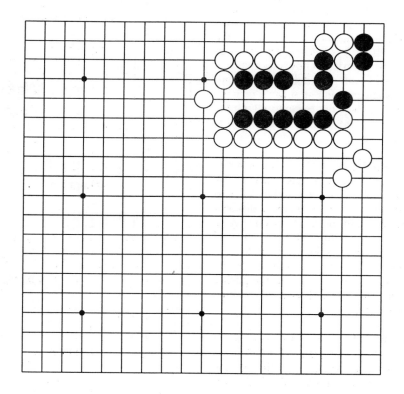

Black has one eye in the center and another in the corner it seems. If white can cut black in half the problem is solved, but one must fully appreciate the possible replies by black.

(12% respondent success rate)

Solution

The Point is in the Response to the Solution

Solution Diagram The point of this problem is to be found in how black responds to the correct first move that white makes in the solution, rather than in the question of how white should mount an attack. If white wants to separate black's two groups of stones, the move at 1 occupies the vital point. Black 2 is answered by white 3, which is satisfactory, but now black takes a step backward with 4, and this is the point. Black aims at capturing at either **a** or **b**, so white has no choice but to capture with the move at 5, and the ko that results here is the correct solution.

Diagram 1 (Black dies) When white plays 1 & 3, black cannot make two eyes by connecting at 4. In response to black's atari at 8, white adds a stone at 9 before discarding them both, and there is only one eye in the corner. Then white 11 & 13 prevent black from making a second eye in the center because of a shortage of liberties. Black is dead. At the move at 11, if white pushes in at 12 instead, black plays at 11, making life for the group.

Diagram 2 (Black lives) If white starts action by making the hane at 1, black plays at 2, which forces white to add the move at 3. With the moves through 6, black lives easily.

Diagram 3 (Simplistic) Playing the hane at the head of black's two stones with white 1 in the expectation that black will respond at **a** is all too shortsighted. When black cuts with the move at 2, capturing at either **a** or **b** are equally attractive options [miai] for black.

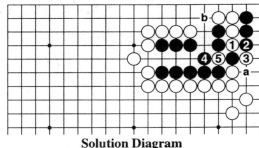

Solution Diagram

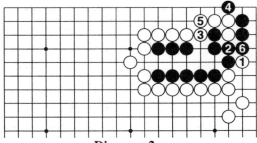

Diagram 1

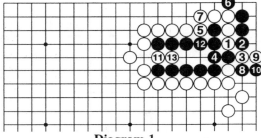

Diagram 2

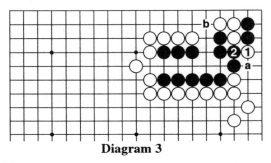

Diagram 3

180

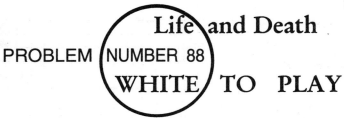

Life and Death

PROGRAM NUMBER 88

WHITE TO PLAY

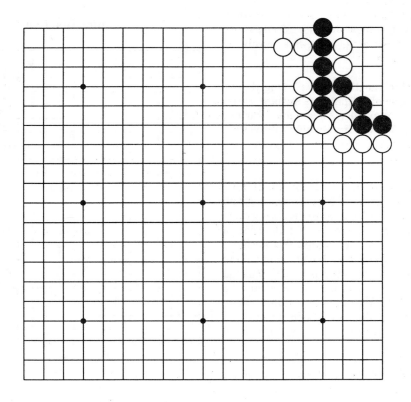

At first sight this looks simple, but there is a large pitfall set up within it. And it is a cleverly conceived problem: if too much precaution is used in avoiding the trap, then one will likewise fail.

(20% respondent success rate)

Solution

With Best Play on Both Sides a Ko Results

Solution Diagram The cut of white 1 is a move which cannot be questioned. Without cutting here, white will be unable to find a place to start to make inroads into the corner. Black 2 and white 3 are also the only moves, both of them. If white uses the move at 3 to capture at **a**, black lives easily by playing at 5.

Well then, at that point playing the diagonal move of 4 represents the best option at black's command. An inevitable sequence of moves follows, from white 5 through 9, resulting in a ko fight, and this is the correct solution.

Diagram 1 (Self-centered reading) If the correct move order of the previous diagram does not come into sharp focus during one's analysis, one is in danger of falling into a trap that is concealed within this position. When white extends to 3, black might think that it is perfectly alright to play atari at with the move at 4, but this is a mistake that is the start of black's downfall. If white captures at 5, black lives with the move at 6. However, white will not be so obliging to play this way.

Diagram 2 (Black meets with a counter-attack) When black plays atari at 4, white ignores it to play a counter-atari from the opposite side at 5. Following the capture of black 6...

Diagram 3 (Black dies) White plays the throw-in of 7, and with the straightforward variation through 11, magnificently wraps black up and captures the whole group outright.

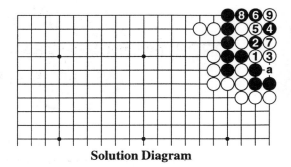

Solution Diagram

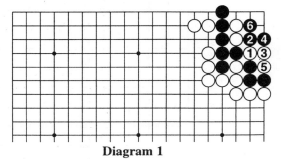

Diagram 1

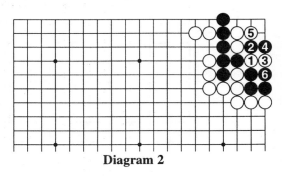

Diagram 2

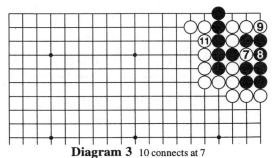

Diagram 3 10 connects at 7

182

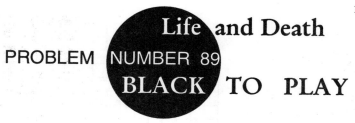

Life and Death

PROBLEM NUMBER 89

BLACK TO PLAY

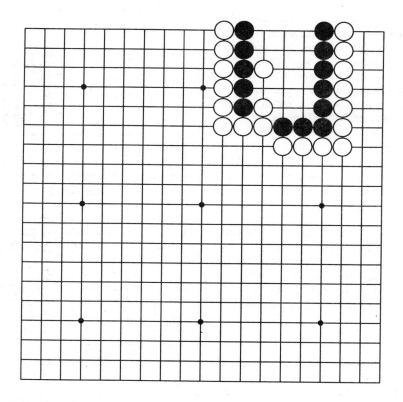

Even if black's five stones are captured, insuring two eyes for the stones to the right will be fine.

Turning the position into ko would be a failure. Please make life for the group unconditionally.

(21% respondent success rate)

Solution

A One Point Jump is the Vital Point

Solution Diagram Trying to save the five black stones to the left at all cost will lead to failure.

The jump to black 1 is the one and only measure that will lead to salvation. If white pushes in at 2, black 3 sets up conditions for making one eye at the upper area of the group and one at the lower. When white plays at 4, black 5 leaves white with the problem of dealing with the cutting point at **a**, which prevents white from further pursuing the quest of depriving black's group of eyes. Consequently, white will capture black's five stones with the move at **b**, and black will make life for the group by playing at **c**.

Diagram 1 (White suffers a loss) When black makes the jump to 1, if white plays the move at 2, black connects at 3 and is able to save the five stones. After white 4, black lives with 5. Instead, if white plays 4 at 5, black is given the opportunity to play at **a**.

Diagram 2 (A ko fight) Turning at black 1 is just the sort of move that attempts to save the five stones at all costs. The hane of white 2 results in black's liberties rapidly being filled, and after white plays at 6, black cannot avoid a ko fight.

Diagram 3 (Black dies) The attachment of black 1 is poor form. When white makes the moves at 2 & 4, black's group dies quickly and easily.

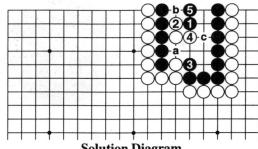

Solution Diagram

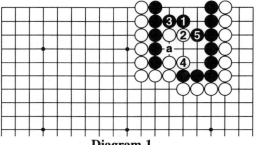

Diagram 1

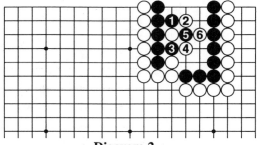

Diagram 2

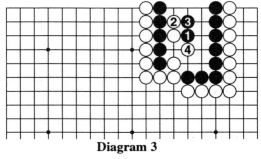

Diagram 3

Life and Death

PROBLEM NUMBER 90

BLACK TO PLAY

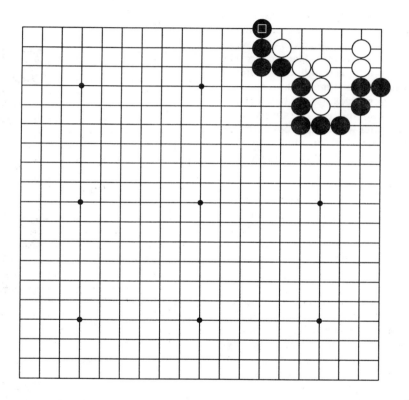

Although the area is tight here, the variations are complex.

In the end, the descending move of the marked black stone plays an exquisite role.

(22% respondent success rate)

Solution

Sacrifice Stone Strategy

Solution Diagram Ending up with a ko fight here would be failure. There is a move available to kill white's group of stones unconditionally.

Black starts by exchanging 1 for white 2, and then turning to play the attachment of black 3 follows an important order of moves. When white connects at 4, black plays the diagonal move at 5, and although white is able to capture these stones with 6 and the following moves, black has deliberately set white up to do so: this is the main point of the problem. After white captures at 10, the placement of black 11 kills white unconditionally. Please confirm this for yourself.

Diagram 1 (A variation) When black attaches at 3, if white answers with the move at 4, it is sufficient for black to descend to 5. White 6 is refuted by black 7, which makes **a** and **b** equally effective alternatives [miai] for black and white's group once again dies.

Diagram 2 (A ko fight) Black cannot kill white's group unconditionally with the placement at 3. After white plays the move at 4, black's move at 5 is now countered by white 6 & 8, setting up a ko fight. If white plays 8 at **a**, black of course answers at 8, returning to the position in the **Solution Diagram**.

Diagram 3 (Another ko fight) If one is looking for a ko fight in this situation, then jumping in to black 1 is better. When white responds at 2, black plays atari at 3, and in the sequence through black 7, a ko fight in which black has even less at stake than in the previous diagram is unavoidable.

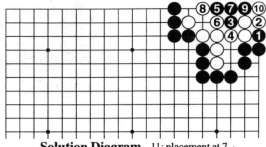

Solution Diagram　11: placement at 7

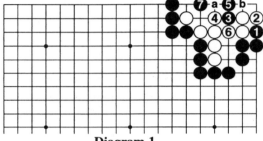

Diagram 1

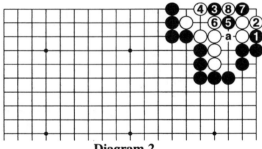

Diagram 2

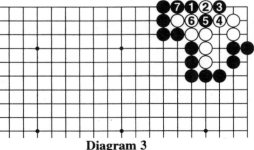

Diagram 3

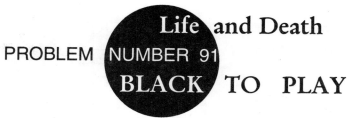

Life and Death

PROBLEM NUMBER 91

BLACK TO PLAY

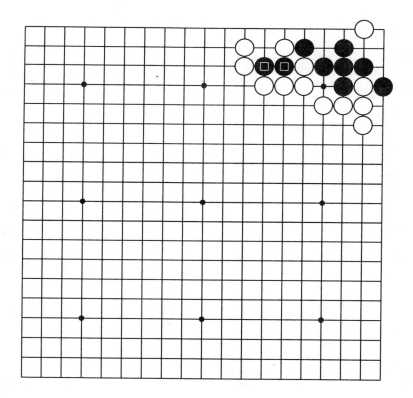

As might be expected, the black group cannot live unconditionally.

The matter will be settled by finding a way to utilize the two marked black stones, which are irretrievably captured.

(19% respondent success rate)

Solution

An Unexpected Forcing Move [Kikashi]

Solution Diagram When contesting a ko fight, there is a big difference whether, under the same conditions, that ko turns out to be a direct one, or an approach move ko. The correct solution here finds an exquisite move of black's ushering in a direct ko.

Starting action with the poke at black 1 is actually quite an interesting line of play. If white captures at 2, connecting underneath at black 3 is the key: where there was one stone before there are now two. In the continuation through black 9, a direct ko is produced. If white 2 is simply played as the atari at 6, black answers at 5, and even though white can now capture at **a**, the ko that will be fought is a direct ko.

Diagram 1 (Seki) It is unreasonable for white to make the placement at 4 in the expectation of killing black outright. This black group has liberties available on the outside, so with the moves through 7, the position becomes seki.

Diagram 2 (A one move approach move ko) The black hane of 1 and defensive retreat to 3 also results in a ko fight. However, in this position it is necessary for black to play two moves, at **a** and at **b** in order to resolve the situation. In other words, what we have here is a one move approach move ko.

Diagram 3 (Black dies) Descending to black 1, and then making the moves at 3 & 5, is a strong line of play that aims at making unconditional life for the group. But white can follow with the atari at 8 and black will not succeed.

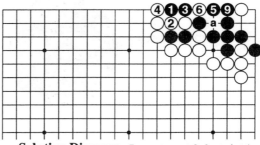

Solution Diagram   7 recaptures at 3; 8: atari at 1

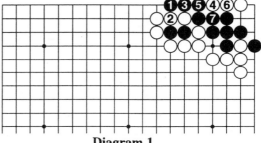

Diagram 1

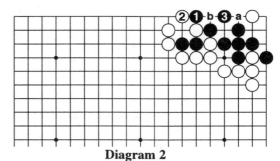

Diagram 2

Diagram 3   9 takes at 5; 10: throw-in at 8

188

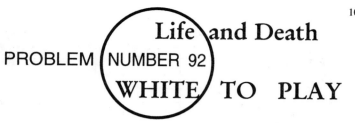

Life and Death
PROBLEM NUMBER 92
WHITE TO PLAY

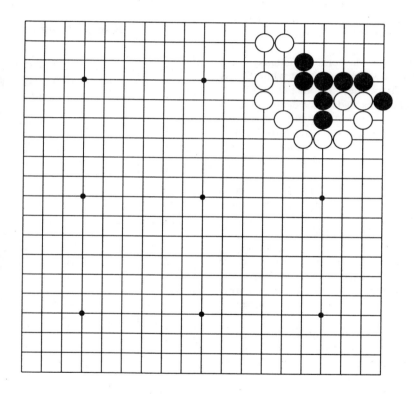

Black has a roomy shape. Should white play inside that position, or attack from the outside? The mandate is to kill the group unconditionally.

(24% respondent success rate)

Solution

The Vital Point is a Large Knight's Move

Solution Diagram White 1 is a move that advances as far as possible into black's corner while still retaining a connection to the white stones on the outside. In short, the large knight's move of white 1 strikes at the vital point of black's corner.

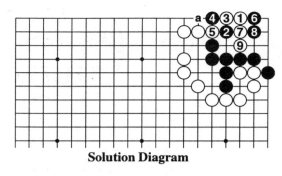

Solution Diagram

Black puts up desperate resistance with 2 and the following moves, but white lightly brushes this aside, and an inevitable sequence of moves leads to the death of black's group after white 9. Along the way, if black plays 6 at 7, white exchanges 6 for black 8, and then playing white **a** leaves black with insufficient space to make two eyes.

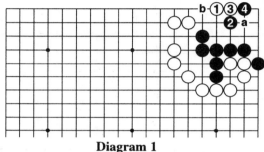

Diagram 1

Diagram 1 (White fails) It is not good enough for white to play the more shallow thrust against the corner with the knight's move at 1. When black responds at 2 & 4, white is afforded no further scope to put pressure on black's corner. Even if white cuts at **a** next, black answers with the atari at **b**, and white's play is shown to be unreasonable. Please confirm this for yourself.

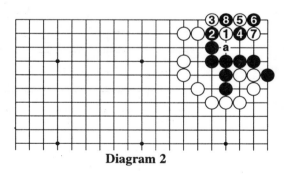

Diagram 2

Diagram 2 (A ko fight) Common sense suggests that the best way to attack would be by jumping in at white 1, but here that move does not work out well. After pushing at 2, black makes the attachment of 4, and with the moves up to 8, black sets up a ko fight. If black plays 6 as the atari at **a**, white answers at 7, with the same result.

Diagram 3 (A lack of liberties) When black plays at 4, attaching at white 5 is even worse. Black follows the proper move order from 6 as shown, and after black plays 16, white lacks the liberties to kill black.

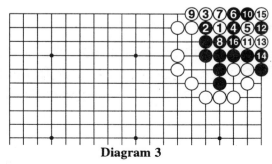

Diagram 3

190

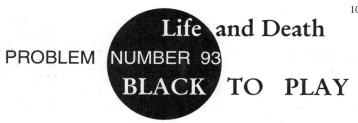

Life and Death
PROBLEM NUMBER 93
BLACK TO PLAY

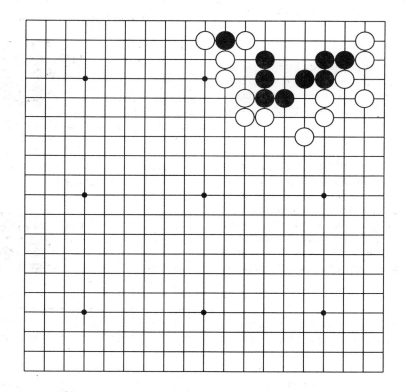

Black's position is painfully difficult, being open at the edge on both sides. Playing in a straightforward manner simply to make two eyes will not turn out well.

Find the vital point for the first move. Making the position into ko would be a success.

(38% respondent success rate)

191

Solution

The Vital Point is a One Space Jump

Solution Diagram Jumping to black 1 here is the vital point. It is natural for white to jump in with the move at 2, so black can play the sequence from 3 through 7, using the proper order of moves to produce a ko fight.

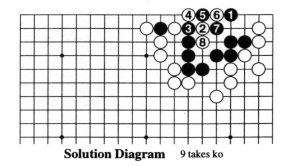

Solution Diagram   9 takes ko

If black starts the sequence by playing at 7 instead of 3 & 5, the result is also ko, but in that case it would be white's turn to take the ko first, so one must exercise caution here.

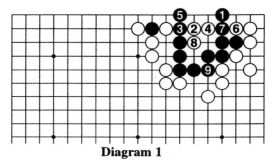

Diagram 1

Diagram 1 (Seki) When black plays the move at 3, it is unreasonable for white to shun the connection underneath at 5 and play at 4 with the aim of giving white a dead, oversized eye shape [nakade]. After black plays at 5, even if white attacks with the 6 & 8 combination, black connects at 9, and there is no better outcome than seki that can be attained.

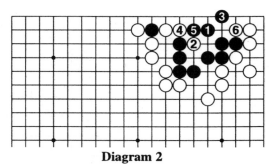

Diagram 2

Diagram 2 (Failure for black) If black plays the diagonal move at 1, white 2 strikes at the vital point of black's eye shape. Black might try to live with the diagonal move of 3, but it is already too late. White attacks from the outside with 4 & 6, and black ends up completely annihilated.

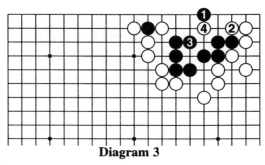

Diagram 3 (Another failure for black) Playing at black 1 also displays poor form. White again attacks from the outside with 2, and after black responds at 3, white 4 leaves black without any recourse.

Diagram 3

192

PROBLEM **Life and Death**
NUMBER 94
BLACK TO PLAY

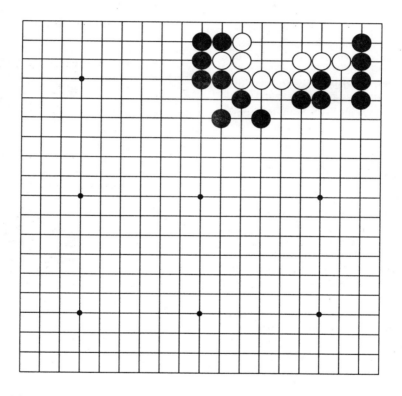

It does not seem like there is anything worrisome about white's eye space. However, by attacking the vital points in the correct move order, the group can be killed unconditionally.

This is quite a difficult problem.

(2% respondent success rate)

Solution

Play a Hane First, Then a Placement

Solution Diagram The hane of black 1 might seem like a hopelessly commonplace move, but playing anywhere else will give black no chance of unconditionally killing white's group. White 2 gives tenacious resistance, but black makes a placement at 3; then black 5 follows an important order of moves to prevent white from making two eyes. Now one must avoid getting tricked by white's attempt to get more space with 6. Black makes the attachment of 7 first, then connects underneath at 9, magnificently ringing the life out of black's stones.

If white plays 2 at 3, black slides to 2, and once again white cannot make two eyes.

Diagram 1 (Premature) After playing the sequence that starts with the hane at 1, black might answer white 6 by connecting underneath at 7 here, thinking that this is acceptable. However, that is a mistake. When white captures at 8 & 10, black has a sticky problem to deal with. The move at black 11 is answered by the connection of white 12, which is the vital point in this situation. Following the sequence through black 15...

Diagram 2 (A ko fight) White 16 sets up a situation where rapidly disappearing liberties costs black five stones. Then, after the five stones are taken off the board, black plays atari at the point of 19, and the end result is a ko fight.

Diagram 3 (Another ko fight) If a ko is what is desired, there is no need to play such a complex variation. It is simpler to slide in at black 1, and from the attachment at white 2 through black 7, that is what we have here.

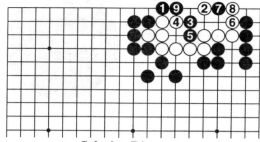

Solution Diagram

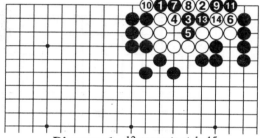

Diagram 1 12 connects at 1; 15 captures at 7

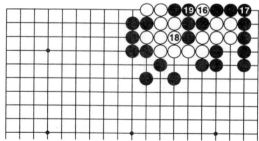

Diagram 2 20 captures; 21: atari at 19; 22: makes ko by playing below 19

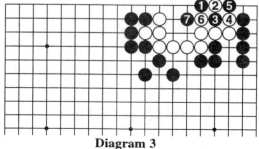

Diagram 3

194

The Endgame

PROBLEM NUMBER 95

BLACK TO PLAY

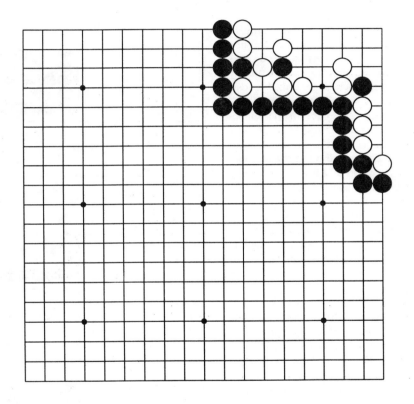

There are no ko threats that may be played else-where on the board. Considering this section alone, the question is posed: what are the best endgame moves for black and white?

(27% respondent success rate)

Solution

Start Operations from the Inside

Solution Diagram It is unsatisfactory for black to play humdrum endgame moves in this position, encroaching a step at a time from the outside. Instead, this is a situation where black has to start action within white's group with the move at 1, threatening to precipitate a race to capture [semeai]. When white hanes at 2, black cuts at 3 and plays atari at 5. It may seem that black is merely throwing away stones here for a sizable loss, but whatever has been lost so far will be more than compensated for in the subsequent play. It is inevitable that white play the attachment at 6, and the unforked variation through 12. If white plays the move at 10 as the connection at 11, black can play at **a**. After black takes the ko at 13...

Diagram 1 (Three stones are captured) Lacking suitable ko threats, white must give way with the move at 14, and then black is able to capture three stones with the move at 15.

Diagram 2 (White in a losing ko fight) When black cuts at 3, white cannot answer by playing atari at 4. After playing atari at 5, black plays at 7 in order to capture the four white stones below. Even if white plays 8 & 10 so as to start a ko fight, white has no ko threats, so playing this way is unreasonable.

Diagram 3 (A loss of 2 points) After black plays the atari at 5, white might capture at 6, reasoning that even if black pushes through at 7, white's groups can live independently. However, compared to the **Solution Diagram**, the variation played here is 2 points worse for white.

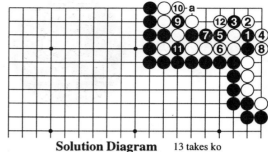

Solution Diagram   13 takes ko

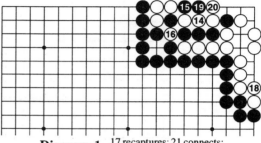

Diagram 1   17 recaptures; 21 connects; 22: atari below 14; 23 connects

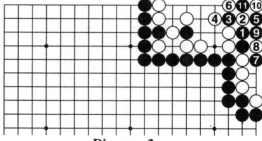

Diagram 2

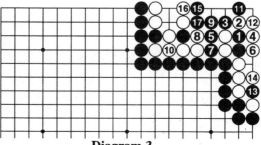

Diagram 3

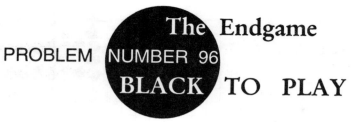

The Endgame
PROBLEM NUMBER 96
BLACK TO PLAY

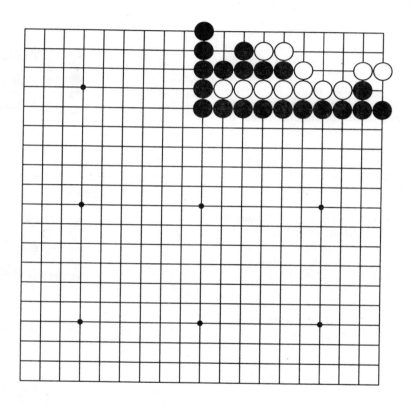

This problem asks the reader how many points of territory white will be able to realize in the corner.

The point to be made is in black's first move, but dealing with white's reply requires precision.

(23% respondent success rate)

Solution

White's Territory Amounts to 8 Points

Solution Diagram Starting action with the cut of black 1 in this position is a skillful finesse [tesuji] in the endgame. It is natural for white to defend at 2, but then black makes the placement of 3, playing in the correct move order here. If white connects at 4, black makes a connection underneath with the moves at 5 and the following, and white's territory is found to be 8 points. This is the correct solution. Within this variation, if white plays 4 at 8, black replies at 6, and then the sequence white **a**, black **b**, white **c**, black **d**, white 1, and black **d**, leads to seki. Also: if white considers playing 6 at **a**, it must be understood that afterward, when black fills in the liberty at **d**, it is necessary to add a move at white 6.

Diagram 1 (White's territory is 10 points) Even though the cut of black 1 is the correct move, trying to squeeze white with the moves at black 3 & 5 results in failure. Playing black 9 after this is ineffective, and when white cuts at 2, the white territory here amounts to 10 points. [Note, however, that white ends in gote here. Presumably that gote is worth more than 2 points.]

Diagram 2 (White's territory is 9 points) If black pokes at 1, white connects at 2 and the variation proceeds up to black 11. At some point, white will be forced to add a stone at **a**, so the territory white controls here is 9 points.

Diagram 3 (Again 9 points for white) Starting activity with the placement at black 1 also invites a loss. When black cuts at 3 and plays the endgame moves through 9, white's territory is again 9 points.

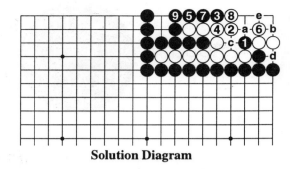

Solution Diagram

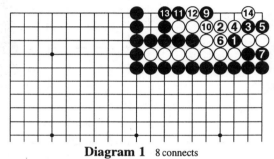

Diagram 1 8 connects

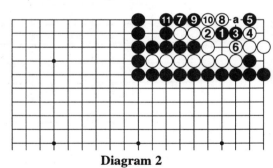

Diagram 2

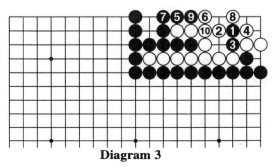

Diagram 3

198

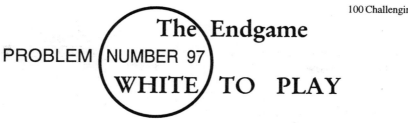

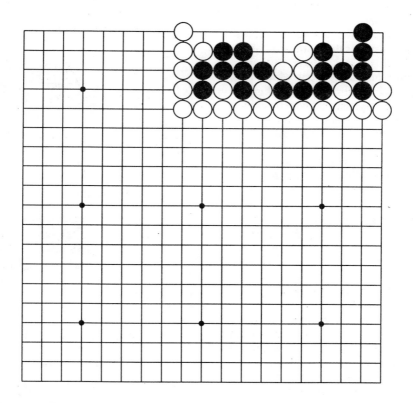

It may be thought that no matter how one plays, the endgame result will be the same, but depending on how one makes one's moves, a 2 point difference arises.

White 1 & 3 are exquisite moves.

(9% respondent success rate)

Solution

Connecting at the Base is an Exquisite Move

Solution Diagram Playing the hane of white 1 is the first step towards the correct solution. In response, black 2, making bad shape, is the best answer. However, at that point, white connects at the base of the group with 3, and this move is a skillful finesse [tesuji] that illustrates the main point of this problem well. Black will have to make a response here no matter what white does, so perhaps black realizes that blocking on the right side at 4 is best, and with the moves through 8, black consolidates 11 points of territory. This is the correct solution.

Diagram 1 (Black's territory is 10 points) When white hanes at 1, if black plays the atari at 2, then white plays 3 & 5 in sente, and is able to turn to play the move at 7. The result is that black's territory amounts to 10 points. In effect, simply responding with the move at black 2 has lead to a 1 point difference.

Diagram 2 (Now black's territory is 12 points) When black plays the move at 2, if white just answers in a trite way by crawling at 3, black will block at 4. The ordinary endgame sequence following white's move at 5 leads to black securing 12 points of territory. If white uses the move at 5 to connect at 6, black replies at **a** and the result is the same.

Diagram 3 (Again black's territory is 12 points) If white starts operations from the inside with 1, it will not prove to be profitable. White's one stone played at 1 will ultimately become a sacrifice, meaning that black's territory here can be calculated as 12 points.

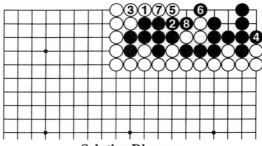

Solution Diagram

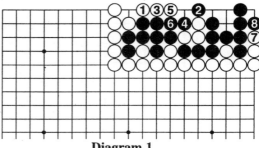

Diagram 1

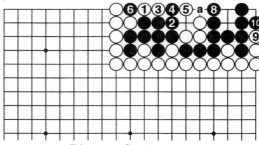

Diagram 2   7 recaptures

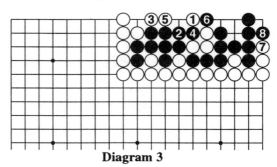

Diagram 3

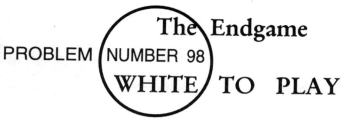

The Endgame

PROBLEM NUMBER 98

WHITE TO PLAY

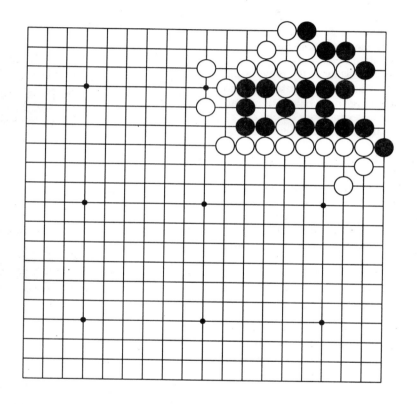

How should one play endgame moves against black's corner? The order of moves is important, but there are points to consider in black's replies as well.

(12% respondent success rate)

Solution

Half of the Black Group
Ends up as Seki

Solution Diagram In this problem, one is faced with the question of how to best take advantage of black's shortage of liberties. To do so, it is essential that white first fix the shape with the moves at 1 & 3. After that, cutting at white 5 is a severe move, which must be met by black's adoption of the technique of descending at 6, putting up the greatest resistance. By playing the moves from 7 through 11, white fixes the shape so that the position below turns into seki. Above, black's territory can be calculated as 4 points.

Diagram 1 (Big failure for black) If black is unable to discover the descending move of 6 in the **Solution Diagram**, suffering a large loss is the prospect. White cuts at 1, and when black takes the stone with 2, white 3 & 5 secure the corner. Should black play 2 at 3, white 2 would make the situation critical for black.

Diagram 2 (White ends in gote) If white cuts on the other side at 1, one might be deceived into thinking that the result is the same. However, after white sets up the seki situation with the moves through 9, there is no need for black to respond, giving up sente. There is a tremendous difference between ending a sequence in sente or in gote.

Diagram 3 (Strong play) If black is determined to take sente here, the connection of 2, sacrificing five stones, is best. [Note: black's move elsewhere must be worth at least 10 points.] There are situations where playing black 2 here would be better than following the variation given in the **Solution Diagram**.

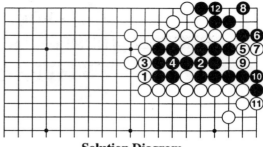

Solution Diagram

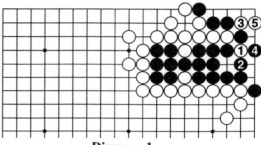

Diagram 1

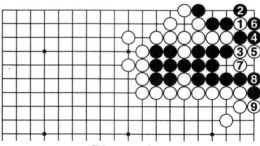

Diagram 2

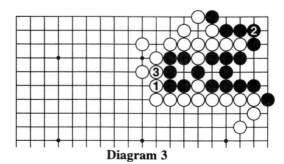

Diagram 3

The Endgame

PROBLEM NUMBER 99

BLACK TO PLAY

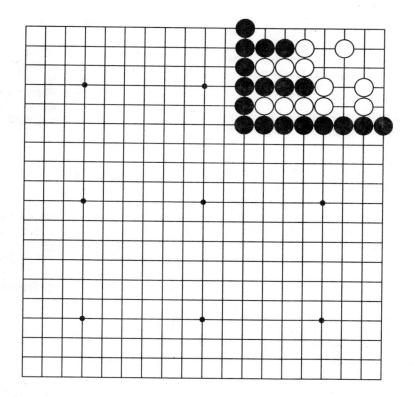

Where should black begin endgame operations and what move order should be followed?

Without regard to which side ends up in sente and which ends up in gote, in just this area find the endgame moves from first to last.

(18% respondent success rate)

Solution

Cutting into the Position is a Skillful Finesse

Solution Diagram Cutting at black 1 in this situation is a skillful finesse [tesuji] in the endgame. If white answers at 2, black will then get the opportunity to make the attachment at 3. Plagued by a shortage of liberties, white will perhaps draw back to 4, and then the rest is easy. Black plays the sequence from 5 through 9, leaving white with a territory of 8 points. This is the correct solution.

Diagram 1 (Black gets the last move in) Playing the move at white 8 in the previous diagram as the block at 1 in this diagram is a mistake, since black gets to play the last move in the sequence with the hane and connection of 2 & 4. The upshot is that white's territory is again 8 points, but black has been able to make a point as well, and considering that fact, white has suffered a loss. Playing the endgame well means that one cannot relax until the last move has been gotten in.

Diagram 2 (White incurs a 1 point loss) When black cuts at 1, if white answers at 2, attaching at black 9 is no longer an option. However, with the moves from black 3 through 11, white ends up by incurring a 1 point loss.

Diagram 3 (Black suffers a 1 point loss) If black fails to make use of the skillful endgame finesse [tesuji], and merely follows the commonplace sequence from 1 through 7, white's territory turns out to amount to 10 points. Black's territory is 1 point. Consequently, when compared to the **Solution Diagram**, the sequence shown here is 1 point inferior for black.

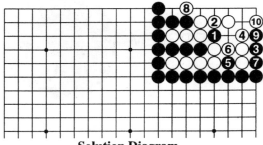

Solution Diagram

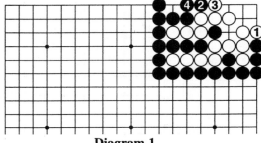

Diagram 1

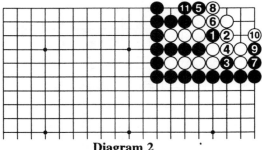

Diagram 2

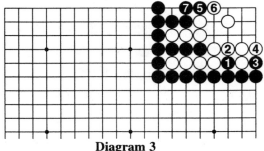

Diagram 3

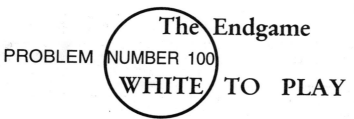

The Endgame

PROBLEM NUMBER 100

WHITE TO PLAY

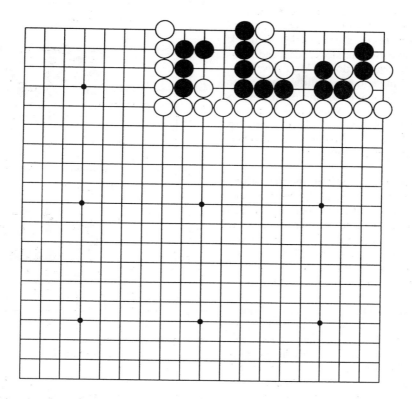

White's stones within black's territory cannot be rescued. The problem inquires how white can manipulate matters to cost black the most points in being forced to take the white stones off the board.

Show the best endgame moves here to the finish.

(14% respondent success rate)

Solution

Wrapping Things Up in the Proper Move Order

Solution Diagram The best way to proceed in this situation is to play the commonplace move at white 1, pushing into black's position. When black responds at 2, white takes advantage of the chance to wedge into black's position with 3, utilizing black's shortage of liberties. If black wants to save the four stones, descending to 4 is the only way to do so. After this, playing white 5 in the corner follows the proper form. If one manages to find the moves so far, the rest is simple. White plays the moves from 7 through 13, and black winds up making 14 points of territory in this corner. This is the correct solution.

Diagram 1 (Shortage of liberties) When white plays the wedge at 3, trying to capture at 4 is wrong. White 5 suddenly saddles black with a shortage of liberties, and the four black stones cannot be rescued. Even if black captures at 6, white will play **a**, black **b**, and white **c**. If black plays 4 at 6 instead, white replies at **d** and the result is the same.

Diagram 2 (One-sided reading) Should white adopt the technique of playing the hane of 1, black must take care in making a response. Black responds with the moves at 2 & 4, and when white plays the atari at 5, if black answers with the move at 6, white is able to capture the corner with the moves through 9. But this is too much for white to expect.

Diagram 3 (No move for white) When white plays atari at 5, black must have the resourcefulness to discover that the diagonal move of 6 makes the proper form. This one move captures all of white's stones.

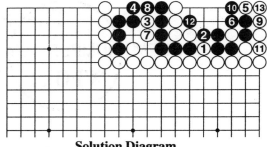

Solution Diagram

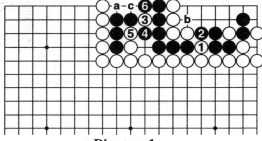

Diagram 1

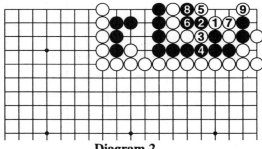

Diagram 2

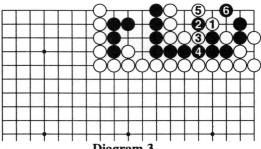

Diagram 3

Glossary and Index

Japanese Terms

[aji] *defects in a position that can be profitably exploited* 20, 24, 28, 39, 54, 57, 76, 86, 89, 90, 94, 96, 100, 138

[aji keshi] *a move that mistakenly eliminates possibilities for making profit or damaging the opponent's position* 26, 54, 74, 82

[furi-kawari] *an exchange, often forced by circumstances, whereby one swaps territory or stones for a similar amount of the opponent's* 18, 34, 144

[kikashi] *a forcing move* 18, 46, 54, 56, 76, 80, 132, 142, 154, 188

[kori-gatachi] *overly concentrated shape* 76

[miai] *a pair of moves which are virtually equivalent in value, and either of which one is guaranteed of occupying* 50, 64, 66, 70, 74, 100, 116, 180, 186

[moyo] *a large territorial framework* 11, 12-14, 19, 20, 26, 27, 32, 48, 68

[nakade] *an oversized eye which can be filled in such a way that two eyes cannot be made* 166, 172, 174, 192

[sabaki] *deft play that makes the most effective use of the stones that one has played; often used to deal with an opponent's burgeoning position* 10, 30, 34, 37, 38, 44, 48, 52, 56, 73, 82-86, 89, 90, 97, 98, 100, 101, 102, 107, 110, 112, 114

[semeai] *a race to capture, with both sides attempting to kill the other's stones* 44, 46, 58, 64, 68, 80, 86, 118, 132, 139, 141, 142, 147-150, 152, 154-160, 171, 172, 176, 196

[shinogi] *deft play insuring the survival of one's stones* 67, 91, 92, 146, 170

[tesuji] *a skillful finesse that exploits the possibilities in a position in the most effective manner* 18, 28, 74, 85, 96, 100, 111, 112, 114, 118, 122, 134, 140, 156, 166, 178, 198, 200, 204

A

atari *a move that threatens to capture one or more of the opponent's stones on the next move* 24, 26, 32, 36, 38, 46, 54, 56, 60, 62, 64, 66, 70, 71, 76, 80, 86, 88, 90, 92, 94, 102, 104, 106, 108, 110, 114, 122, 128, 130, 132, 136, 138, 144, 146, 152, 156, 158, 162, 170, 172, 178, 180, 182, 186, 188, 190, 194, 196, 200, 206

attach/attachment *a move played in contact with the opponent's stone; often used in conjunction with sabaki, q.v.* 16, 18, 24, 30, 32, 42, 44, 50, 52, 56, 58, 62, 64, 68, 70, 74, 78, 80, 82, 86, 90, 92, 96, 98, 100, 102, 114, 118, 120, 124, 128, 130, 134, 148, 152, 158, 160, 162, 166, 172, 176, 178, 184, 186, 190, 194, 196, 204

B

bad shape *an ineffective move, such as an empty triangle* 74, 102, 148, 160, 200

big point *a move that is the biggest on the board in the opening* 16

C

cross-cut *a technique used to cut an opponent's stones apart; often used in conjunction with sabaki play* 24, 52, 56, 75

E

endgame *the final stage in the game, when the size of moves can be calculated most precisely* 108, 127, 128, 195, 196, 198-201, 203-205

exquisite move *a move that is unexpectedly effective* 124, 130, 154, 160, 188, 199, 200

extension *a move that extends one point from an adjacent stone; also: a developing move that expands one's position* 8, 30, 36, 60, 62, 70, 76, 90, 112, 122

G

gote *a move that is necessary for one's position but which the opponent need not answer; opposite of sente, q.v.* 10, 198, 202, 203

H

hane *a move that curls around an opponent's stone or position* 8, 10, 14, 24, 26, 28, 32, 34, 38, 40, 42, 52, 56, 68, 72, 74, 78, 80, 82, 83, 86, 90, 95, 98, 100, 105, 106, 114, 122, 126, 128, 130, 132, 134, 136, 142, 146, 148, 150, 152, 154, 158, 162, 168, 170, 174, 176, 180, 184, 188, 194, 196, 200, 204, 206

hanging connection *an effective way of connecting that takes advantage of the fact that the opponent will avoid discarding a stone at that point* 38, 58, 94, 128, 152

J

joseki *a sequence of moves, usually played in the corner, that yields an equal division of territory and/or thickness* 7, 8, 78

K

knight's move *a standard shape that can be effective in attacking* 12, 24, 26, 30, 82, 90, 100, 190

    attaching (or striking) across a knight's move 44, 46, 178

ko *a situation where one cannot capture a stone that is in atari until one plays elsewhere on the board* 20, 38, 40, 42, 46, 50, 58, 60, 76, 91, 92, 94, 112, 118, 121, 122, 126, 128, 130-132, 135, 136, 140, 142-146, 148, 150-154, 156, 158, 160,

162-166, 168, 172, 174, 176, 178, 180, 182-184, 186, 188, 190, 191, 192, 194, 195, 196

L

ladder *a repeating atari situation that snakes in a zigzag pattern across the board*
26, 34, 63, 64, 101, 102, 109, 138
ladder break *a move that is played in the path of a ladder in order to break its operation*
64, 138

M

middlegame *the portion of the game after the opening where the most intense fighting takes place; often considered the most difficult phase of the game* 16, 22, 33, 36, 37, 39, 41, 43, 45, 47, 49-51, 53, 55, 57, 59, 61, 63, 65, 67

O

opening *the earliest phase in the game, roughly lasting through the first thirty or so moves of the game* 7-9, 15-17, 19, 21-23, 25, 27, 29, 31, 62, 122

P

pincer *a move that squeezes a stone of the opponent's between two positions of one's own*
8, 12, 28, 78
placement *a move that occupies a vital point inside the opponent's position*
24, 40, 42, 124, 132, 136, 140, 150, 154, 160,
162, 166, 172, 174, 176, 178, 186, 188, 194, 198
proverb *one of 65 or so go proverbs that convey traditional insights about the game into a pithy phrase*
"Take the critical point rather than the big point." 21
"If one's real intent is to play on the left, feint to the right." 69
"Play a knight's move in response to a capping move!" 90
"Capture the cutting stone." 98
"Add a stone to one on the second line before sacrificing them both." 170
"Strange things happen at the 2-1 point." 172, 176, 190

S

seki *a position where neither side has two eyes, but neither can attack the opponent's stones further without encountering self-destruction* 42, 126, 188, 192, 198, 202
sente *the initiative, the right to play first, a move that must be answered by the opponent; the opposite of gote, q.v.* 8, 16, 28, 38, 96, 108, 132, 142, 168, 200, 202, 203

T

thickness *a position that has few weaknesses, such as cutting points; thickness equates to power across the board* 8, 10, 18, 22, 28, 32, 66, 84, 88, 90, 104
throw-in *a sacrifice stone often used to reduce the opponent's number of liberties* 118, 128, 132, 144, 152, 156, 158, 164, 168, 170, 172, 174, 182, 188

V

vital point *a point that is essential for one to occupy to stabilize one's position, or to attack the opponent's* 10, 14, 22, 26, 28, 30, 42, 44, 56, 68, 90, 102, 126-128, 147, 148, 150, 160-162, 166, 170, 172, 174, 176-178, 180, 184, 190-194

Other Books on Go from Yutopian

Fighting Ko
by Jin Jiang

This handbook catalogues the wide variety of ko situations that one is likely to encounter over the board, as well as several that may not appear in the courseof a lifetime of playing! But the reader will appreciate the concise and thorough treatment of the subject.

Some players shy away from playing ko because they fear that they will get lost in the complications, but in the final analysis, this fear stems from a lack of understanding of the fundamental concepts involved. **Fighting Ko** provides all the information, advice and encouragement the reader may need to overcome such limitations.

Ko positions in opening, middlegame and endgame settings are shown, as well as those that arise in standard *joseki* and invasion sequences. Strategy and whole board analysis as they apply to ko fights are also covered. The special properties of the 1-2 and 2-2 points in the corner, often utilized in making ko, are given elaborate treatment as well.

In addition, several examples from professional games are presented. The final chapter tests the reader's comprehension of the material covered, offering twenty problems similar to ones that may occur in real games circumstances.

Mastering the subject matter presented in this book will add potent weapons to any player's game.

Nie Weiping On Go
-The Art of Positional Judgment

Written by the strongest and most famous player in China, this work is also the first Chinese go book ever translated into English. In the biographical section, Nie's arduous struggle to become one of the finest players in the world is recounted, as well as his hardships during the Cultural Revolution and the stirring account of his challenge of the Japanese domination of the go scene.

This book is divided into eight chapters: The Opening, Positional Judgment, Timeliness of Initiating Battles, Finesse and Trade-off Decisions, Forcing Moves, Utilizing Thickness, Defending Weak Stones, and Applications in fully Annotated Games.

All of these themes are woven together by Nie and given a masterful interpretation that will help every go player in analyzing the demands of a position.

A Compendium of Trick Plays
The Nihon Kiin

In order to get stronger, go players will often spend a lot of time studying joseki. However, experienced players know that this may or may not work out as expected. One can easily devote hours studying long sequence moves but understanding the variations only imperfectly. When one tries to apply what one has learned, one ends up incurring losses inexplicably. "Learn joseki and get two stones weaker" is a satiric "go proverb" that contains a great deal of truth. Worse, joseki books that are available in English are out of date, and many of the variations in them are no longer considered valid. One might learn a long sequence of moves to no purpose.

But the variations explored in **A Compendium of Trick Plays** are to be encountered in any go club. They are sequence that have been played since time immemorial, and will continue to be played forever. **A Compendium of Trick Plays** is jam packed with classic "sleights of hands", cunning trickery and straightforward advice on how to meet these moves effectively. In the first chapter, Ishida Yoshio, the former Meijin/Honinbo, and renowned for his joseki dictionary, gives a comprehensive overview of the subject. Chapter 2 is written by Kageyama Toshiro 6 dan, one of the most popular of go writers. Chapter 3 is Mihori Sho's contribution. (He is the writer who worked with Sakata Eio on **Killer of G0**.) The final chapter, a collection of 25 problems to test the reader's understanding, is by Maeda Nobuaki 9 dan. A unique extra feature is a 4 page cartoon by Fujii Reo. A translation guide offers a fascinating glimpse into the structure of the Japanese Language.

Killer of Go
by Sakata Eio, Honorary Honinbo

A legendary work by a legendary player... **NOW in English for the 1st time!**

"Razor-sharp" Sakata, so long at the forefront of the go world, produced, when he was at the height of his powers, a classic text on the theme of killing stones.

This work went through more than 100 printings in the late '60s!

Sakata conveys, with exquisite erudition, the thrill of the chase and the satisfaction of the winner when a well-planned attack bears fruit. At the same time, he offers a thumbnail sketch of the history of go through the ages, masterpieces of attack from his own and others' games, fascinating glimpses into the nature of offbeat joseki and the shape of stones, as well as classic games which he fully annotates. One is the famous game between Meijin Shusai Honinbo and Karigane Junichi, alluded to in the Dictionary of Basic Joseki, Vol. 3, page 4, as "the famous 'group-capturing masterpiece' played between the top players in the team match between the Nihon Kiin and the Kiseisha in 1926. It is celebrated as one of the most difficult matches of all time."

Sakata also fully annotates the first game he played without a handicap against Go Seigen. Neither of these games have ever been available in English before.